CALICO BOYS

by

LLEWELLYN JENKINS

LC

*For my family, of course, and for
Meadow and Celia*

Leaping Cat Press

First Published in 2002 by Leaping Cat Press

Copyright 2002   Llewellyn Jenkins
The moral right of the author has been asserted

Typeset in Dutch Roman
Printed in England by Barnwell's of Aylsham, Norfolk

A CIP catologue record for this book is available from the
British Library

ISBN 0-9543336-6-0-8

Leaping Cat Press
PO Box 25
Harleston
Norfolk
IP20 0ZY

CONTENTS

Then said he: He may well be called Jacob, for he hath undermined me now two times, first he took away my birthright: and see, now hath he taken away my blessing also. And he said, hast thou kept never a blessing for me?

Genesis 27:36 (*Tyndale's Old Testament*)

CALICO BOYS

Part One

SEA TOWN

THE bronze evening light had long been doused by drizzle; black clouds, whipped by a westerly wind, were sweeping diagonally over the Recreation Ground. Most of the others, the bigger boys, had already drifted away, but I couldn't find my jumper, my only school one, and Mum'd told me never to go to the Rec in my school one. I could still make out the spectral lines of the goal at the far end of the football pitch, so I shouted 'Hang on!' at the smudge of Siôn's back, and tore off to see if anyone had dumped the jumper at the foot of one of the posts.

They hadn't. It wasn't under the big sycamore either, so I bent a forlorn eye upon the ranks of fir trees carved out against the storm-hatching sky. I remembered losing a tennis ball in there once. Moments later I was pushing through a tangle of branches and bramble, and sliding down into the shallow trench where the fir trees were rooted. Crouching and shuffling badger-like along its length, I fanned the earth with grubby hands, unearthing Vimto bottles, a cat's skeleton, prophylactics, and even, tantalisingly, a jumper. But not my jumper. Cursing as best I could, I clawed cobwebs out of my hair and sat back on my haunches, my feet spearing soil the texture of brown sugar, my knees nestling

9

between white roots crabbed like a witch's hand. The wind and rain drove at the upper branches, wrenching them hither and yon, and for a while I was a pirate rounding the Horn, my gunwales groaning with doubloons. Then the winds fell, the gloom around me grew ever more intense, and I fell into moody preoccupations with lost jumpers, excuses, and the smile of a girl called Joanna Wilkinson.

A belch of thunder was my alarm call. I lifted my eyes to the arch of branches over my head, but saw no arch, no branches. With sudden misgiving I started crawling up the bank. Fir needles, clogged with rain, shed showers of droplets as I wriggled through the lowermost branches and came up under the sycamore. When I stepped out from behind it, knuckling moisture out of my eyes, something fell through the bottom of my heart and anchored me to the spot.

It was gone.

My world of light and scale had gone, vanished into darkness with depth but no shape; no sound too for a moment, until a far-off cry reached me on a *swish swash* of wind, but softer, much softer, than my own shallow breathing. I took a few frozen paces forward, my eyes straining for anything familiar. Phantom shadows riding buffets of rain sent me scurrying back, and I sank to the ground hugging a goalpost. I remember grass oozing tuftily around the post, the cold earth against my bare knees, and rain slitting the night like a silver blade through black card. I remember the fir trees rearing over me like coffins, starting to cry and salt on my tongue. I'd never felt so lonely in my life.

'Worra you doing?'

As I looked up, Siôn emerged wraithlike through the murk and stood over me, wet as a brown trout, blinking through narrowed eyes. I uttered a faint sound, no more than a croak, and he grabbed my wrist and pulled me up. He didn't say anything, just led me away, his shoulders scrunched up against the wind, giving me little tugs until I fell into step beside him. I held on to his hand for about a dozen steps, then took his sleeve instead. By the time we reached our gap in the fence, most of the rain had gone. There was a scent of pine needles and a fog over the office blocks on the north side of the Rec. Here and there windows were lit in a sparse ascending diagonal. We pushed through the fence, ducked under some bushes of blackberry, and surfaced under the glow of a streetlight. I dropped my brother's sleeve and we headed home.

'I lost my jumper,' I said. 'Mum'll go mental.'

'It'll be there tomorrow. The man in the hut'll find it.'

'I'm soaked.'

'You're bonkers.'

I sniff, in a kind of general agreement. A pause. Then my voice: 'You won't say anything to anyone, will you?'

'No.'

We walk the rest of the way home in silence, kicking a stone along the pavement.

The train lurched forward, recoiled and shivered to a halt. I rasped my knapsack on to Hastings station, jumping out to an expiring whistle from further down the platform. 'Asleep were you?' said a rock-faced business-type. I caught his bleak, angry stare as he shuttled up the window. More whistling, a tattoo of banging doors, then a line of other faces - blank, vaguely antipathetic, a couple of sniggering kids - passed in front of me as the London train recommenced its journey along the south coast. I lit a cigarette and watched it lollop into the mid-distance, judder oilily over a series of points, bank left and disappear from view.

Behind me a guard dipped into a mail bag trolley. I took a deep breath. And another. I was jaded from too much worry and too little sleep, and felt strangely reluctant to move. I wondered if the guard needed a hand with all those parcels. What a wonderful job - hefting parcels, blowing whistles and short-arming doors shut. Soon he would be home, having his tea and watching television. Maybe he had a cat. Just a normal, everyday kind of day for the guard and his cat. I stubbed my cigarette against a post and picked up my knapsack. It was an afternoon in February 1997: a fine afternoon, not cold, with a light wind off the sea drying out some overnight puddles in front of the taxi rank.

On the way to the guest house, the bony youth driving the mini cab munched M&M's, made tiny adjustments to his wing mirror, and acted like he'd been driving a mini cab all his life. Then he got lost. When his radio crackled into life he nearly died. I lay my head back on the seat and stared out of the window. Since yesterday I'd been hiding in the past an awful lot; now I went off somewhere a long time ago, a long way away. I was seven or eight, and it was getting dark after football in the Rec. My brother walked too far ahead of me and I began to lose him in the vaporous gloom.

' - newspapers?'

I looked up. The traffic had slowed to a crawl. The driver's soft-boiled eyes, the blade of his nose, loomed large in the rear-view mirror. He was perched forward on his seat, his jaw angled open.

'You from the newspapers?' he repeated.

I shook my head. The eyes blinked. I said nothing. A little man like a bantam-cock was leading his three kids along the seafront, his massive wife bringing up the rear. They were all wearing Manchester United shirts. When I turned back the eyes in the mirror were still on me.

'They've been lining up at the station,' he said, sounding matey. 'I thought you was another one.'

'Oh,' I said. I should have left it there.

'What's happening with that?' I said.

'Got him. Step-dad. Headmaster an' that.' A strange feeling of loneliness made echoes in my heart. I was back at the Rec. Pitch black. The car leapt forward. 'Hang him, I would,' said the driver. He crunched into second, took a sharp right, then a left. Lines of pink and yellow terraces filled the windscreen, each one a crouching monster.

He decanted me at a guest house about half a mile from the pier: a squat, red-brick affair, built just above street level. As I turned the key to my room, a burst of brittle laughter drifted across the corridor. Through a half-open door, I saw a young girl in a green dress and white knee socks, sitting on the end of a bed and staring down at her feet. In front of her stood a grey-jowled man with his shirt tail hanging outside his trousers. His hair was combed forward to his brow. He was doing the laughing. When he saw me, he stopped laughing and flat-soled the door shut.

My own room was large, well shaped and full of late afternoon sunshine. It also stank of air-freshener. I opened a window. Across the road a dog was cocking its leg against a fence. I lit another cigarette and sank into a chintz-covered armchair. The rug at my feet bore the blotchy pattern of a disease of the flesh. I stared into it for a long time, growing sleepy as the sun leaned low on the crumpled horizon. A copper ashtray set in a strip of suede was draped over the arm of the chair; I wondered where I'd seen one like that before, and remembered the smell of parched air, the beady eyes of stuffed birds, and whisky, warm on my face - a bible, too, a big one, sitting in dust-riddled sunlight. I was dog-tired. I dropped my burnt-out filter into the ashtray, shuffled over to the bed and flopped onto the fat artificial-silk bedspread. The cool fabric swelled up between my nose and the crook of my arm, and I fell asleep.

When my eyes opened, I dozed wakefully for half-an-hour or more, looking over at the big armchair with its loaded ashtray, looking at what is and thinking about what is not. Outside, twilight had faltered into dusk, and foody smells were drifting up through my window. The thought of food made bile rise in my throat. I told myself I needed a cup of tea. As I filled the kettle in the bathroom, the clamourous tones of television news music crashed in from another room, reverberating all around me. It was like a punch in the head. I took the kettle back into the bedroom and plugged it in, flicking on the television at the same time.

I sat cross-legged on the bed, trying to open a packet of biscuits I didn't want to eat, listening for news I didn't want to hear. As the kettle boiled, those grisly shots of my brother appealing for help at the news conference appeared; this was followed by a live broadcast from outside Hastings police station which anticipated him being charged with the murder of his foster-daughter. I muted the set and watched the pictures move across the screen like so many aqueous shapes. Searching my mind for a comforting thought, I found none and sank back onto the bed. It was quite dark now. A crispness had settled in the air. An eddy of wind sent up a little spray of ash from the ashtray.

I shivered and looked for my coat.

First I called at the house where Siôn and his family had been staying with friends since the murder. I knocked. A foreign student answered, holding the door open a few inches, enough for me to see the challenge implicit in her eyes. When I told her who I was, she said no-one was there, no-one was expected, she didn't know anything and that I couldn't come in. The door closed before I could ask for directions to the police station. I went to the nearest pub and asked there. Before long I was toiling up a hill, hugging the curve of a high wall and bristling at the fine rain swinging into my face. I'd brought the wrong coat. It was already heavy with damp as the hill flattened out and I turned into the police station: a flat, boxy building, aglow against the lowering sky, ribbing the undersides of trees like a bonfire.

Assorted members of the news media were scattered across the tarmac in threes and fours. Some were chatting, drinking coffee; one had a mobile phone clamped to his head, another yawned and glanced at his watch. A television crew exchanged cynical jokes; a sallow-faced photographer drew on a cigarette and laughed along. All were adjusted to the climate of waiting. The sense of anticipation was palpable, but essentially the mood was relaxed, good-humoured even, such as you might find outside a football ground where the home side is ahead at half-time. Everyone was dressed for the conditions, mostly in light waterproofs. This was their job. They knew what they were doing. I was soaked, reasonably scared, and didn't know what the hell I was doing.

A cameraman crouched into his shooting stance as a lamp lit up the head of a television reporter. The reporter gave a sneezy chuckle. He braced his shoulders and cleared his throat. There was a brief hiatus as a battery was changed, then he pushed a loose strand of hair away from his face and began a piece to camera, stating with owlish intensity that Siôn had just been charged. Whether this was fact or fancy was unclear, but I felt cold and I felt sick. When he had finished, the reporter shook his head, looked down at some notes and started mouthing the words again, adjusting his delivery for the next rehearsal.

At the glass doors of the station I hesitated. Not for the first time in the last 48 hours I was gripped by an alarming sense of incomprehension. None of this 'it all felt like a dream' nonsense; everything felt real enough, but maybe I was misunderstanding some vital component; maybe all that was missing was a gesture, some kind of contributory emotion from me to make everything clear, to make everything, well, *right*. So outside Hastings police station on that pious February evening, with goose bumps prickling my flesh as sweat evaporated, I thought as hard as I could about what I had heard and seen and felt, and gave the skewed world a last chance to right itself. When it didn't, I went inside.

The pale, functional reception area was crammed with journalists. Evidently the ones outside were the overflow. Everyone was standing. Above a steady rumble of conversation, one or two mangled remarks were being tossed from group to group. I tried to catch something but couldn't; I heard only the rumble and saw mouths moving above steaming cups of coffee. When one of the faces - female, oval, fringed by chestnut hair - turned towards me and brought out an ersatz smile, I found myself metamorphosing into a man who always pops into the station around this time: a ghastly performance which consisted largely of feigning abstraction and making whistling noises through my teeth. Had I met her somewhere? Of course I hadn't, but she had recognised me, a fact as unmistakable as the predatory glint in her eye. I suppose I shouldn't have been surprised, but my resemblance to Siôn has always been far more apparent to other people than to us.

So I'd lost my anonymity. So how, exactly, is the brother of a murder suspect meant to comport himself? Suddenly I found it difficult to breathe; I felt pinned down by the harsh overhead lighting, bullied by the heavy shadows, suffocated in the clammy, odour-ridden atmosphere. Behind me the front doors swung open, and a blast of cold air helped propel me through the human soup to the reception desk. The young WPC on duty was smiling and telling two pressmen - it sounded like she'd said it several times before - that yes, there would be an announcement soon.

As the hacks drifted away, her eyes froze on me. I saw, I thought I saw, that flicker of recognition again.

I said thickly: 'May I see an officer on the Jenkins case?'

'What's your name?' she said.

Her tone sent a chill through me: not because of the hardness in it, though that was present, but because of something else, something I would later come to recognise as evincing a certain brand of moral superiority. The chattering behind me had ceased. Convinced that all ears were now bent in my direction, I was disinclined to answer her question, so I repeated mine with some eye-goggling. She looked at me as if I'd made an improper suggestion.

'Wait there,' she said.

She disappeared through a door adjacent to the

crook of the counter. In less than a minute she half returned, then disappeared again. Two more minutes and she returned completely.

'There'll be an announcement in half-an-hour,' she said.

'I see - if I could see someone...'

'You'll have to wait half-an-hour.'

I didn't argue. I peeled away from the counter and headed for the door, looking neither left nor right till I reached the refuge of darkness. Then I kept going, walking blindly, maybe forty yards or so in a straight line, my heart in my teeth, the muscles in my legs fluttering as I tried not to run. When I got to a shallow wall I slumped against it, tilted my head back, and sucked in lungfuls of clean air laced with sea fog. It felt so good I almost laughed. The rain had stopped. Mysteriously, all but one of the outside crowd had gone. Gone where? - inside presumably, but I hadn't heard them. A single photographer remained: a rangy, vulpine figure, silhouetted against the lighted doors of the police station. He was smoking a cigarette, smoking it coolly, unhurriedly, thinking of other things, his investment in these events little more than the price of a strip of film. He took a final drag - I heard his hissing breath - and flicked the butt away. Fleetingly it described a parabola in the air. Then he drew up his collar, rasped his shoe over the butt, and went inside.

I walked up and down slowly and reflected

rapidly. Perhaps there was a way of bypassing the reception. I took my knapsack over to a nearby lamp and pulled out my mobile. I got through to the station quickly enough. A female voice listened politely and replied ambiguously in monosyllables; a male voice, even cagier, said he knew how I must be feeling. He also told me that I couldn't see Siôn.

I backed out of the light. I was all out of next moves, so I sat on the wall, rested my chin on my interlaced fingers, and stared up at the windows of the police station. Somewhere in there was my brother, up there, inside one of those little cubes of light, breathing in as I was breathing out, so close I felt I had only to raise my voice and he would hear me. My sole purpose in coming to Hastings had been to see him, to let him see me, to let him know he wasn't alone, that I would always be his brother no matter what. I hadn't looked beyond these things. I had failed, and the very air seemed to resonate with my failure.

A car sped by. I watched its rear lights dwindle and lost myself in a tangle of conjecture. I heard footsteps advancing towards me but no response clicked into my brain.

'May I ask - are you Siôn's brother?'

The woman was standing in front of me. Her appearance matched her propriety of speech: I saw cream hair, beautifully cut, an ivory sheen at her cheekbones, a long dark coat with some kind of fur at the collar. A silk scarf at her neck. She looked out of place in that setting, in that scratch-me-down town.

I nodded and she introduced herself and gave me the name of her newspaper. All I gave her was a stroppy look. Her lips parted. Before any other sound emerged I told her I had nothing to say, spitting out the words in little pieces. She looked hurt and took a step back. I paused for a second but it was all too confusing, too awful, and I walked away, away from that place, walking anywhere. Later on, much later, I fancied I'd detected some kindly intent in her approach. Wishful thinking perhaps; it's equally possible that the rest of the hacks in the station that night elected her to go out, reckoning she had the best chance of getting some answers out of me. My instincts let me down on too many occasions around that time to be sure one way or another. It's hardly important, anyway.

I don't remember walking down the hill. I only remember walking, and night settling heavily upon the pavements, and pushing fingers through my matted hair, and walking down a road which crept with drizzle and limpid shadows. And seeing Siôn's face unrolling against the insides of my eyelids when I stopped walking, sat down in an unlit bus shelter, and closed my eyes.

A pissed-up kind of roar jarred the silence. A gang of lads was straggling across the other side of

the road. The shortest of them, his mouth lolling
open like a child in a Breugal wedding feast, kept
lurching over to the kerb, almost but not quite
falling off the edge. Somewhere a shop alarm started
ringing; its long, aggressive peal echoed around the
streets. As if taking a cue, one of the lads gave a
delighted howl and ran off, kicking lamp posts. Two
others gathered up the Breugal child in a prehensile
lock and marched him away, bellowing cheerful
obscenities into each ear. A younger kid followed
glumly in their wake. When they'd gone, I felt
strangely bereft. I reached into my knapsack for
cigarettes, finding everything except cigarettes. A
bus pulled up; its doors gasped open. Light lay
across the pavement like oil, which helped me find
the cigarettes. I shuffled one out of the pack.
Suddenly aware that I hadn't heard anyone
disembark, I looked up.

The driver's face was cupped in his hand. Leaky
eyes gazed out at me from heavy features. I was the
last straw, apparently.

'There'll be nothing else tonight,' he called over.
'Where are you going?'

I shrugged and shook my head. Deep inside the
bus someone laughed: a joyless, cancered sound.
Then the cab light went out and the bus snarled
away, gathering speed as it nosed its way out of the
bus lane. I stuffed the cigarettes back into my
knapsack. I had to go on, had to be moving and

doing. I abandoned the main road, took a series of arbitrary turns and found myself on a short avenue which led to the park: an immaculate stretch of pine, oak and birch, clearing and glade, ridged on all sides by iron railings. A veil of mist lay across it like breath on a window. On the south side, smouldering and undefined, a row of Victorian villas rose above the line of trees, the lights of its upper floors spanning the park like a necklace. A familiar gable-end glowed whitely in the moonlight. Siôn's house. Siôn wouldn't be there, of course, and God knows where Lois and the kids were, but I thought I should go over there. And, like I said - did I say? - I had nowhere else to go.

I appeared to have Hastings to myself. Even the drone of cars had ceased. I heard the prickling of sodden earth in the park, and my footsteps slurring on the road, little else. The drizzle too had ebbed away, leaving a muggy night without any breeze. The town might have been holding its breath. My clothes felt glued to my body. As I crossed into Lower Park Road, I tugged at my shirt and jumper, trying to move some air around in there. I saw flowers leaning against the ornamental wall, most still wrapped in cellophane. On the park side of the road a police notice was attached to the railings. The side entrance had been taped off. I hadn't been to the house for a long time, two years or more, and I'd forgotten how big and tough and ugly it was, how far above pavement level it sat. I crossed back over the road to look at it properly, and remembered doing the same thing during that last visit. I'd been taking a photograph. Siôn was in a T-shirt and trainers, opening up the boot of the car; Lois and the baby were descending the stone steps from the house; Lottie was in the car, waving at me; the other three were all around us, skylarking and giggling and breaking into runs. One good sweet day in the thick of their lives, the sun stoking the sky, the big bow windows dancing with glints, gleams and sparkles.

Now it was a different house. Moon-thrown shadows fell obliquely across the roof as if attempting to hide it away. The dark mass of stone exuded a chill intimacy, and I thought about the hopes and dreams, compromises and sudden violence its walls must have absorbed. The bow windows were saying nothing. They gazed out like great eyes, opaque and implacable, eyes which kept their secrets. Billie was dead. The others in the photograph would never be the same again. The photograph, that day, and my memory of it, were like relics from another time, over forever, leaving only sorrow, pity and an ache of doubt. Billie was dead. My thoughts ran down other alleys of the past as I tried to remember something about her. I couldn't. There was nothing, not a single flash in the void, just an overwhelming sense of the fragility of life. It felt like an offence. A car screamed around the park, its headlights rolling across the ornamental wall and glittering off the clutter of cellophane. When the harshness of the ensuing silence became too much, I walked away.

And then my mobile rang.

I nearly ripped a nail off, unzipping every zip on that knapsack, trying to get to the thing. When I did, it slipped out of my hand, skated over the wet concrete and fell into the road still ringing, the sound echoing crookedly across the park. I walked over to it as slowly as I could, picked it up and punched in a digit. It was my sister-in-law. She was at the police station. She said she needed my help and asked where I was, her voice faltering, almost fading away. I told her. After some back and forth stuff at her end, she came back on and told me a police officer would pick me up in about ten minutes. When she rang off the tensions in my stomach started coiling tighter than ever. Clearly she wasn't with Siôn. So where was he? I wondered where the girls were staying, or if they would be at the police station too. My night, apparently, was only just beginning.

I wandered over to the park railings. All around me lights were being switched off in sitting rooms. I pulled some moisture off a leaf, wiped it across my forehead and fell back on gazing at the house. After I'd taken the photograph, the one I told you about, we'd all climbed into the car and driven across the Downs, stopping off at villages along the way. I know we saw a bicycle race, and I have a picture of the girls meeting a giant Paddington Bear. There must have been a fête on or something. Siôn and I slipped away to a second-hand bookshop, where I picked up a little copy of Cowper's letters. It's just about my favourite book. In one letter he says:

> 'My mind has always a melancholy cast, and is like some pools I have seen, which, though filled with a dark and putrid water, will nevertheless, in a bright day, reflect the sunbeams from the surface.'

I love Cowper. He says things like that: beautiful, wise and sad. On the last evening of my visit, the Cowper in my pocket, Siôn and I took a turn around the park, treading in the footsteps of countless other walkers, the air still heavy with pollen, Siôn talking, the sound of it in my ears all my life.

All the sounds were peaceful as my taxi disappeared and I was left alone on another deserted road in Hastings. In front of me the leaves of a hedge glistened in the street light, emphasising the layer of darkness beyond the hedge. Above that a single star flickered over a copse of old trees. I stared at it for a few seconds, trying to relax my eyes. I'd left my spectacles at home and the backs of my eyes were aching.

CALICO BOYS

The last couple of hours had left me in a state of nervous inertia. It had begun in a police car, with a silent driver and flashlights smacking into the roof like shellfire; shouts followed, then a scream and a high, smoky whisper which came from nowhere and made my skin crawl. The next part was echoing back stairs, swinging doors and my sister-in-law, her tears corralled within an arc of wrinkled shirts and closed expressions. I gave her a hug, and got a few questions in, but mostly I listened. Then another back seat, more flashlight, and being driven too fast along greasy streets, where I lost all sense of time and place, and where we ripped a wing mirror off a parked car.

Before long - forty, maybe fifty minutes after being picked up - I was back at the guest house, and there an age-old weariness filled me. I closed the door and listened to my breathing, suddenly conscious of my chest rising and falling. I switched off the light, lay on the bed and looked towards the wall. Outside my room the fluid world still beat on: a smear of conversation here, a snatch of laughter there, but inside my head very little registered above the roaring currents of doubt and retribution.

Siôn rang a few minutes before midnight. He told me what I already knew, that he'd been released on police bail, and gave me an address. After that the giddy throbbing at my temples at last began to abate; and now, as I crunched across private gravel towards the copse of trees, I felt a curious sense of optimism. My footsteps sent pigeons threshing through branches and over the roof of a low, sprawling house hidden from the road. My brother, disgorged from the back of a police station with a carrier bag and the clothes he stood up in, had found many doors closed to him. But not this one.

I went to the back door and tapped lightly on the door frame. A porch light was switched on, the door opened and a woman's face, gentle and overwrought, appeared briefly, smiled, then melted away. And there, suddenly, was Siôn, shoulders hunched, beaming weakly across the threshold. The sight of him braced me. In that moment, too, I felt a seam of private apostasy closing up.

'Hello brother,' he said.

We hugged in a badly organised, half-embarrassed way, then he led me down a narrow hallway into a living room cramped by shadows. In the better light, settled in the corner of a sofa, I looked at him properly. The flesh on his face had sunk in off the bone, and there was something sick and haunted within the triangle of his mouth and eyes. He sat very still in a low armchair, his hands clenched in front of him, his lips pulled tightly together. It was a while before he spoke. When he did, it was with an air of plunging:

'Look here, how much do you know?'

'Too much. Not enough.'

He stared at me blankly for a moment, as if trying to get some further meaning out of what I'd said. A quick expression of irresolution passed over his face. Then he nodded and brushed his hands together as if they had sand on them. For some reason I noticed his nails. All the time we were growing up he used to bite his nails; sometimes they'd be bitten down to the quick, the flesh around them raw and bleeding. Then he left home and didn't bite his nails anymore. It was the damnedest thing - there we were, in the midst of all that, and I couldn't stop looking at his nails, thinking about why he'd stopped biting them. Or why he'd started. I thought I should know something like that.

He asked me about the police.

'They told me they couldn't hold you any longer,' I replied, 'that you either had to be charged or released on police bail. You're supposed to leave Hastings. I think the idea is that I take you.'

'The police,' he said. 'You wouldn't believe...' His eyes left mine and strayed around the room, not seeing much. Then he began to tell me about his arrest and about the hours of interrogation, but I heard little indignation or outrage in his voice, just, it seemed to me, a sort of emphatic bafflement. And as he talked, I found myself keeping a watch on him from within the centre of myself, perfidiously looking for anything unfamiliar. There was nothing, though I felt the weight of the years we hadn't shared.

When his words fell into a pause, I said: 'I've seen Lois.'

He nodded quickly, his eyebrows raised, as if to imply that my seeing Lois was somehow besides the point; and in the explosion of silence which followed I sensed something competitive and uncertain in the air. He rose and crossed the room. I stayed put, staring into the vacant space he'd left, waiting for him to say something. Eventually I half-lifted my head. His back was to me, his arms folded tightly across his chest, and I saw the reflection of his etiolated face in a mirror. His eyes were shut. Save for the fact that his jaw muscle was bulging slightly, he looked like a man drowned.

'Mum and Dad are okay,' I said.

'Good,' he said. 'That's good.'

I squeezed my brain, but there was nothing more to say. He'd already lost so much, you see. No matter what happened from now on, he'd already lost so much. It would not come back again.

'Come on - let's get some fresh air,' I said.

There was a wincing change of expression. He took a deep breath and turned back into the light. His eyes were open now, but downcast.

'Would you like a coffee?' he said.

'I'd like a coffee when we get back. But I'd like a walk now.'

'Yes, I'd like a walk.'

Later, as we walked along the silent avenues of

31

pollarded trees, perhaps then, when I was more clear-headed and he was at his most exposed, I should have asked some more questions. But he'd been asked so many questions, and to of asked them at all would have been to overturn the whole logic of our relationship. Or perhaps I'm just making excuses. All my life I have stood back from things. So we just walked, he and I, an island of peace in a stormy sea, the echoes of our footsteps mingling under a wasting moon. When we'd last walked these streets, children from his school had nudged their parents and called out 'Hello, sir!' and giggled or blushed. One time he'd even driven me out to the school itself, and shown me around with a brisk, proprietorial air, proudly detailing the school's successes in cricket as woodsmoke drifted across the playing fields. He had come a long way to attain the security and respect he craved, and now, amid the silences and rhythms of his speech, I brooded on the nature of fortune and the plenitude of love, and on the mutability of both. There were no stars left in the sky, and for some reason that made me sad too.

We returned to the house and drank some bad coffee. Its taste was the taste of those two days. It was very late, so I drank the coffee quickly, then felt bad when I saw that Siôn had barely touched his. Before I left him outside the porch, he said, very quietly:

'You know I won't leave without seeing Lois and the girls.'

I nodded. His eyes were fleshy with fatigue - just slits, really. But they gazed out at me with real devotion. My throat tightened.

'I'll do what I can,' I got out. 'Try and get some sleep.'

I took another circuitous route back to the guest house. From its silent depths I culled my reasons for optimism down to something credible and called my Dad, who was strong and assured, and called a friend, who was out. After that my brain reached out for the next thing, but couldn't get there. Too tired to undress, still staring at the telephone, I flopped down onto the bed. Around 4.00am I woke up with a mouthful of bedspread. For a few moments I let myself imagine it had all been a dream, but that was never going to work, so I got up and rinsed the taste of Siôn's coffee out of my mouth. I looked in the mirror and tried out a reliable face. It didn't look too reliable. It didn't look young anymore, either. I slept raggedly for another hour or so, then took some biscuits over to the armchair and watched skeins of light breaking up the eastern sky. Bits of things began to float across my mind, mostly about growing up, and once or twice I nearly dropped off. I should really have gone back to bed, but decided to sit in the armchair and await the return of fear.

Later that morning, in the house among the trees, Siôn was reunited with his family and brought one part of his life, perhaps the best part, to an end. The next time he'd see them would be at a Social Services unit in Hailsham. Strangers would be present. The chairs in the Victims' Suite would be placed at 'appropriate' distances from each other, and each nuance of behaviour would be monitored by video cameras and more notes added to a case file. And then Siôn would be arrested and taken to a car and later charged with murder. By then the split with Lois would be final, and Siôn would never live with his daughters again, but continue to exist in their hearts, in photographs and letters, and as an obscure regret which lessens over time but never dies.

Thinking back to that last morning in Hastings, I don't know if Siôn felt that something was recoverable: it's possible. Remember that, in his own way, he loved Lois, and that she had never let him down in anything that mattered. But in those minutes before the children arrived, the room was heavy with disintegration. It weighed on my shoulders when I took in the tea; I saw it reflected in Lois's pale, writhen face, and read it plainly in her eyes. There was nothing left, nothing. Siôn was he, no longer part of we, a person quite detached.

Afterwards, I made a call to my Dad, and between us we sorted out the trip back to my parents' home in Wales. I tried to inject some oompahpah into this, but it was all pretty difficult. On the taxi ride to Lydd airport, there was something awful in Siôn's refusal to see things at their face value, in his determination to build on scraps, but perhaps by that stage a measure of fantasy was necessary for him. I was still weighing this as I stood by the perimeter fence and watched his small plane lift off the ground and rise unsteadily above the Kentish marshes. A departure like that is almost bound to have a strong, characteristic flavour. This one did. There was a glint of hard light on the fuselage, then big clouds floated across the sun, the engines gunned westwards and Siôn slipped from my sight, his course set for Wales, my Dad's waiting car and a future none of us could foretell. I listened to the distant throb of the engines until I was sure the wind was playing tricks; then, and only then, did all my strength seem to desert me. I felt emptied of everything. Behind me, the taxi was still waiting. The driver had his cap tipped over his eyes. I was in no kind of a hurry either, so I lit a last cigarette and watched the sun waning pallidly across the deserted airfield.

Oh, you remember the summers. You remember the hot summers, motoring down to the sea in Dad's Zephyr, the dark green one, before the white Zodiac, the taste of Quells in your mouth; or, rather, of the jam Mum crumbled the Quells into, which just reminded you of Quells and made you sick anyway - remember, those little pink pills for travel sickness, the sickening crunch when you bit into them, all mixed up in the strawberry jam?

'Is he all right?'

'Mum, gunna be sick.'

'Stop, Dai, anywhere!'

Before you're sick you stick your hand out of the window until your fingers are frozen, but afterwards you're okay, at least you can't taste the Quells anymore, so we peel the backs of our legs off the plastic seats and play the car game, staring tensely into the oncoming traffic, wanting to spot the designated radiator, wanting to be first...

'Morris Oxford!'

'Wasn't!'

'Was!'

'Wasn't, was it Dad? Austin Cambridge, wasn't it Dad?'

'Shut up, you lost!'

'Didn't.'

'You're fat. You've got a scar, scarface.'

'Wah!'

'Siôn! Now you say you're sorry.'

'But Mum, he...'

'Siôn!'

Red-faced you turn away, choked by words unspoken, rage unspent. Did you hate me in those moments, your indulged younger brother, protected by all, even by you? If you did, I never knew it; no clouds appeared in my bright blue sky. I knew that I was loved, suspected no ill-will, distrusted no-one. How could I know that you were living a different kind of life, that your sense of injustice was hardening around you like cartilage, your pride growing ever disproportionate to circumstance? How could I know, and where does it come from now, this understanding, this remorse?

Once arrived, we're given our shilling each, and chase each other along the seafront, dodging trestle-boards advertising donkey rides, skirting deck chairs four deep with old ladies showing their drawers and sucking ice cream. On the sunless side of the pier we come to a panting halt opposite the amusement arcade. Its name is spelt out in broken light bulbs. With a little surge of pleasure we cross the road and enter an unaccountable atmosphere of sin. All around us, shrouded figures are moving in patternless activity, breathing in the musty aroma of dead flowers, or, more exactly, the water dead flowers are found in. It's all here, everything we remember from last summer: the ranks of one-armed bandits, coiling and spitting; the glass-domed racing game wherein Piggott, Wragg and the rest eternally spin; the mountainous wedges of copper, still primed to topple at the next roll of a penny, or the next. And along the far wall, to which is fixed an antediluvian tannoy, are the glass-fronted cabinets offering Victorian melodramas of murder and execution, this time to the strains of 'Sugar, Sugar' by the Archies. In the middle of the floor, under the feeble light of a many-branched electrolier, a blocky man with baby ears is sitting in a booth and doggedly picking his nose. He's also reading a newspaper. Behind him is a soft-focus photograph of an Alsatian in a gilt frame. You slip a coin under the grille and address the top of his brindled head:

'Shilling's-worth, mister.'

Before the eyes have risen from the paper, an elbow pivots above a stack of pennies. An odd face grows steadily odder as he yawns without opening his mouth, then fat little fingers divide the stack into two and pass the two stacks across the grille. As you go off in the direction of the racing game, I step forward and give the man my shilling. He smiles a smile as thin as thread. Observable in his eye is a faint gleam. I don't smile back, just watch his fingers stroking the top of another stack. The knuckles are cushioned by tiny rolls of fat, the nails glossy and tapered. He leans forward into an arc of light, his skin shining like oil paint.

'Lovely day,' he murmurs, the voice Welshly-warm, quite refined really.

I say nothing. With a silent laugh, he pushes the two stacks of pennies towards me. His hands travel with the stacks and stay put. At the same time his eyes lock onto mine before lifting, almost imperceptibly, to a spot over my shoulder. I'm not touching the coins with his hands there, so I twist round to see what he's looking at. All I see is a shadowy corner and a door standing discreetly ajar.

It's a cold unhappy moment. But when I turn back
the hands are gone, so I scoop up the money and run
over to join you at 'The Execution of Charles Peace'.

In ten minutes flat my shilling's gone. I'm
watching little plastic horses whirling around a green
baize track, watching them and balefully wondering
why Harry Wragg only wins when I'm not backing
him. I don't know where you are. The glass in front
of me fogs up, and I smear it with my chin. A
disembodied head is wavering over my shoulder. I
straighten up. The reflection looms bigger and
clearer until I'm looking at the blocky man from the
cash booth. I don't turn around, just go on tracking
Harry Wragg.

'How're we doing?' he says, standing beside me
and looking down at the game. I can't speak; fear
holds me as firmly as any shackles. It's a funny thing
though, he's nervous too. I can hear him taking deep
breaths. I feel his heat and smell his sweat mixed up
with cheap aftershave. I sense a certain power over
him and already I'm less afraid.

'Let's see now,' he says, lowering his voice. He
starts feeding coins into the slots, into all the slots,
lighting up all the little bulbs: the green, the red, the
blue, the orange. The coins are just tokens; they
have no value for this man other than as a dubious
means to a dubious end. His fat white fingers are
shaking. I steal an upward glance and see a boil on
his whiskered double chin, badging him with his own

corruption. Suddenly, a glittering windfall of copper shudders into the silver tray in front of me, to the accompaniment of a hissing breath and a crooning 'Wi-nnn!' from the blocky man.

'There you go,' he says. His eyes roll libidinously and the corner of his mouth twitches. 'Take it,' he says, nodding at the tray. 'Your turn.' His belly is going in and out like a scummy-smelling tide. I give a quick shake of my head; he's trying to involve me in something I don't understand. My curiosity, though, is beginning to outrun my fear. I even feel the edge of a sinister exhilaration. And then I see you, standing behind the man's elbow, a scowling picture of fraternal vigilance. You would have been nine or ten.

'Finished?' you ask.

The change wrought by your arrival is remarkable. Before your unwavering gaze the blocky man becomes a ghost to be blown away. His whole body starts shaking. He attempts a smirk, then leans and almost falls against one of his fruit machines. Before our very eyes he appears to be melting into a pool of sweat. I watch, fascinated; I don't suppose I'd seen a grown-up act that way before. Apart from some throat clearing and desperate looks towards his booth, little else happens. Eventually you say something like: 'Let's go, get some sweets,' and I follow you out into the vivifying air, unhurt and unafraid. We get some candy floss from a nearby cabin and I drift back, not going in, just hanging round the entrance of the arcade. The blocky man is collecting his contaminated winnings from the racing game. His eyes are closed and his lips are moving. I can't be sure, but I think he's weeping.

That afternoon we have our first swimming lesson. The tide pounds at my knees, but it's all right; I'm happy enough in the shallows with the squelch of bladderwrack between my toes. You're treading backwards into the swelling waves, Dad by your side, your arms outstretched. You're far away from me now, crucified against the sky and pier, and look! - the water is lapping your chin. Above the clamour of gulls I can almost hear your short jerky breaths, and through the wobbly heat see your eyes, frightened and beseeching, scanning the shore. A cornet arrangement of 'Goodnight Vienna' strikes up from the bandstand. I don't want to see any more, and retreat to the tideline. A leggy, solemn-faced girl of about my age is cartwheeling along the foreshore. She's doing it beautifully, this cartwheeling, giving herself to the flow of movement, her hands and feet hardly grazing the sand. I wonder who she was; I wonder if she ever did anything as beautifully again. She passes two boys playing cricket with a tennis ball - 'I'm Basil Butcher' 'Bagsy me Sobers' - as you and Dad push back through the waves. A soggy matchbox floats into the basin of a rock pool, resting there with my reflection.

Tea, sweet and scalding from a thermos, is taken behind a windbreak of damp towels and blankets. There's a wasp in the butter and sand on my hardboiled egg. A couple from Birmingham - 'Put booket and spade in't boot, Ronnie' - are packing their seaside things into a battered Ford Anglia. Reclining against the bonnet is the solemn-faced girl from the beach. She's eating a Bar Six, pausing now and then to push errant strands of hair behind her ear. Her parents don't ask her to do anything, and she doesn't speak to them, appearing to accept their proximity more or less on sufferance. When they're ready to go, the girl rolls the silver paper from the Bar Six into a ball and glides into the back seat. She leaves the door open. Her father shuts it. As they back out of their space, the window winds down and the little ball of silver paper is flicked out. It bounces off the promenade and lands in one of the sandshoes I've just taken off. My wonderment at the girl's self-containment returns in a sharpened form; then she's gone, and we're on our way home.

I'm doing the crossword in my *Daktari* annual. You're reading an *Incredible Hulk* comic and biting your nails. You haven't spoken since the swimming lesson, but I'm used to your silences, to the muscle fluttering along your jaw, and I know when to leave you alone. Suddenly my brain feels woozy. I can't focus on Clarence the Cross- Eyed Lion anymore. Bits of speech reach me: 'Have you seen that...

rubbish? ... front cover? "We eat flesh", I ask you...
spend pocket money on? At least Llew's book has
proper stories...'

It's about you. I think about another car game.
I'm still thinking when my head gets too heavy for
my shoulders and starts nodding back and forth. I
see the moon, a pale hemisphere of cinnamon and
grey, cartwheeling over Mum's shoulder.

Then nothing.

Part Two

OTHER WORDS FOR SORROW

The day begins as each day of the trial has begun. My nose is squashed against the carpet, I've nearly rubbed an ear off, and I experience a vague, half-waking period in which I know I'm not at home, but can't remember where, exactly, I am. As my brain scraps the last remnant of a dream, I'm hearing footfalls on the thick carpet and a scraping of curtain rings. I blink; sunlight stings my eyes and makes patterns against the back of the sofa, about four inches from my nose. As usual, the mattress of sofa seats has come apart. The bedclothes are rolled up alongside me in a nylon rope. I lever myself up on to one elbow and switch off my alarm. Above the arm of the sofa I see Dad moving around the kitchen nook, making the morning tea, looking touchingly vulnerable in his lilac and green striped dressing gown. He doesn't sleep much these days: three hours a night, four at most. Since this business began he's taken to plugging in his earphone at five o'clock to listen to the World Service, after which he dozes until seven o'clock and Earl Grey. An orderly man, he finds comfort in such rituals.

This morning a deep crease has appeared on his brow. His face is grey and drawn. As the kettle boils, he stands, shoulders hunched, gazing down at the backs of his hands, looking every one of his sixty-three years. Watching him lazily, silently, I'm suffused with a kind of tenderness. He pours the tea, splashing in just the right amount of milk, rather less for him, rather more for Mum. Cups and saucers and Rich Tea biscuits are arranged marshally on the tray. He looks up, sees me:

'Cup of tea, Llew?'

I shake my head and give him a slow smile. The creases in his face fade away. My Dad. I've been relying on him all my life, one way or another. We have this understanding, he and I: it's something we guard, something we tend carefully. I don't expect to know another love like it.

He makes his slippered exit limping slightly; his hip's stiff this morning. I unwind and clamber on to the filleted sofa, trying to shrug off bad sleep. The morning sun is shining through the tall French windows, falling in dust-laden bars upon matt-black wood, blue seat coverings, and the uncared-for clutter of a third-floor flat bought to be rented out. On a shelf unit, next to a cheap figurine of a Greek peasant, sits the growing pile of letters addressed to our landlord. His whereabouts is as much a mystery to us as it is to his creditors: tight-voiced individuals with Midlands accents who ring at odd times of the day and night. I roll up my bedding, push the seats back into the sofa and push the sofa back against the wall. By now I'm wide awake and jumpy. This morning I even hear Siôn's shower starting up. I walk the room with caged strides, trying to locate some of the poise vouchsafed me last night. It's no use. Fear is shrivelling my heart. There's a metallic taste at the base of my tongue. Today's the day of the verdict.

I yank the French windows open, letting in the clean, early smell of the sea. The sun has risen above the chalk cliffs. Now it sparkles across the water and glows off the brickwork surrounding this tiny inlet of Brighton Marina. I step onto the balcony and thread my fingers through its sinuous ironwork. Away to my right, two gulls are planing and circling; another flaps above the hull of a cabin cruiser. Below me, a solid bird with uneven tail feathers is honking at its companions as it walks up and down the freshly-painted jetty, putting its feet down like ready money. Someone passes across the empty space behind me. I look away for a moment. When I look back, my seagull has gone. All that's left is a faint cry rising eastwards towards the sea; just the faintest cry, like nothing had made it, like it came from nowhere and went nowhere, as if the seagull had never been on the jetty at all.

Back inside, Mum is fixing Siôn's breakfast. Her face is wan, bruised-looking. She's brought a shopful of Trout Hall tinned grapefruit from Aberystwyth: Siôn's favourite. Now she's placing segments carefully in a bowl, doing it with love, this simple act, concentrating on the spoon, the tin, the bowl, all the

47

time breathing with enforced steadiness. Dad is behind her, dressed now, moving untidily behind her back, gathering toast from the toaster. Her elbows are raised and he can't reach across to the marmalade. He waits, making a parade of his waiting, until we hear the soft opening of a bedroom door. Our bright good mornings clot in the heavy atmosphere as Siôn walks in, flat-backed and square-shouldered in a crisp white shirt. He slips his suit jacket over the back of a chair.

'Is this tie okay?'

'It's fine,' I say. He seems distracted for a moment and stares through me, making the superfluous gesture of wobbling his tie-knot. Then he nods and walks over to the breakfast table. Three sets of eyes follow him with speculative regard. His body has retained its aplomb, but his face is puffy and wrinkled around the eyes, and his jaw muscles are rippling under sunburnt skin. It's been over a year since he slept without tablets. He sits down and uses the handle of a spoon to trace shapes on his table-mat, his expression carrying a steady, opaque quality which could betoken faith in the future, the workings of Faith, or the impacted regret of a lifetime. As Mum arrives with his grapefruit, making an heroic effort to twist her pain-tightened lips into a smile, Dad halves and quarters the toast, his chest rising and falling with the deeper movement of his heart.

The talk over breakfast is of nothing: talk which is just talk, talk which fills the emptiness and stills the grinding activity of our minds. All that needs to be said is plain to each of us and doesn't need saying. The telephone rings like cold death. Dad answers it, his replies as formal as incantation. The security men are on their way. Mum makes up some sandwiches and places them and a Twix in Siôn's document case. When the door buzzer sounds Siôn puts on his jacket; quiet, curiously remote. We muster for the parting, each of us embracing him in turn, but mentally he is already beyond us, back in the brawling antipathy of the mob outside the courthouse in Lewes. I remember the words I had on my lips last night, made in darkness for him and for this moment, but they won't do. He looks out at me from his hidden world, a smile trying unsuccessfully to settle itself on his face.

'See you later,' he says, the words achingly insufficient for what they say. Three of us leave the flat. As Dad accompanies him down in the lift, I walk along the landing to the big window and look down. There, its engine running, its chrome glinting, is the Range Rover. Alongside it are two suited men in a state of hostile watchfulness. The small one with the hard body and sharp, strong features is shielding his eyes from the sun; the fleshier, graceful one is standing by the gaping back door, his hands folded quietly in front of him. He has half an ear missing. I find this reassuring in a security man.

CALICO BOYS

In a ritual seasoned over four weeks, Siôn emerges into the sunlight and steals a hurried glance up and down the road. The security men like him by now; they make encouraging faces as he lobs his document case into the back seat and jumps in after it. More nods and smiles, the smiles rather grim today, are exchanged with my Dad before they disappear behind smoked glass. The clunk of car doors punctures the steady throb of the engine. The clatter of a winch draws my gaze beyond the wasteland of car park, beyond the blocks of flats, into a thin blue sky. Up there, far above the tortured racket of our lives, a giant crane, mobbed by seagulls, mournfully sweeps the horizon of sea and sky.

Little else stirs as the Range Rover swings out of the driveway, casts off the shadows of the flats, and starts snaking through the gross landscape of Brighton Marina. It passes the Italian restaurant, the Asda supermarket and the petrol station, before taking a momentary pause at an unmanned barrier: the only blemish in its otherwise unbroken rhythm. Behind me I hear the lift opening up and Dad's feet padding back to the flat. At the sound of the door closing I feel a sharp pang of loneliness. Leaning further into the window, straining my eyes, I follow the Range Rover past the bowling alley, past the cinema; following it until there is nothing left to follow, and all I'm looking at is the clouded glass in front of my face. I wipe it with the fleshy part of my palm and look back down the road.

Over at the Italian restaurant, a young waiter I've seen before is positioning tables under a striped canopy and showing off to his girlfriend. She's sitting on one of the tables, her bare limbs shimmering like a bloom on fruit. Indolently she inspects her fingernails, watching the boy sideways. When he's finished with the tables, he goes over to her, and, with a slight bow from his narrow hips, whispers something. The girl's body tenses: wide-eyed with pleasure or shock she utters a strangled shriek and twists off the table. The boy laughs, spreading out his hands as she walks over to the restaurant window, her shoulders proudly arched. Once there, she assumes an almost classical pose until he touches her hair with his fingertips. She gives him a dig in the ribs, not upset at all, and they walk back into the restaurant half-laughing, their faces full of vitality, receding into the happinesses and sorrows of their own lives.

We must have taken a taxi into town that morning because we always did. We would have gone to our usual café - bogus-French, bottled preserves everywhere - and had a coffee. We wouldn't have talked much. We would just have drunk the good coffee and thought about Siôn in our different ways, and coped in the same way; coping because the alternative to coping is not coping which is no alternative at all.

We went to Brighton Art Gallery - yes, to kill time, but also because I wanted to take another look at three paintings Mum and I had seen earlier in the week. The first was a large portrait by Sickert, the second an evocative study of a 20s dandy - a lover of Osbert Sitwell, apparently. But the one I really wanted to see was entitled 'Spanish Landscape'. It shows a cart track winding across a puma-coloured foreground into a range of hills, first tiger-striped then spotted, before melting into scorched tiers of caramel, orange and yellow. Here was the essence of Spain: its vigour, its profundity. It was a beautiful painting. I'd wanted to see something beautiful. Later on, when it was all over, I wrote to the gallery asking for some information on the artist. His name was Wyndham Tryon, he was born in 1883 and died in 1942. Beyond this little is known of him. In the words of the Keeper of Fine Art 'he is not an artist who is terribly well rewarded'.

As we left the gallery, I saw the freelance journalist who'd spotted me in the Lanes during the first week, the one I'd shaken off in the glassware department of Hanningtons. I remembered his narrow commercial eyes, the faint vomitory odour on his breath. I didn't say anything to Mum and Dad, but kept my eye on his reflection in a shop window as we hailed a taxi. Then it was back to the stifling atmosphere of the flat, to the long wait, to a swamp of weariness and suspense, to long walks taken in turn and to an embittered sense of insufficiency.

I took my last walk at 3.30, heading out along the sea-wall and skirting the harbour as Siôn and I had done the night before. There was a still a considerable swell out to sea, but unlike last night the harbour was as still as glass, the only sounds the sloshing of petrol in the fishing boats and the crying of gulls. When I reached the end of the sea-wall, I pulled myself up on a stone ledge and looked down on to the glare of the sea. Gulls were making quick-moving shadows on the surface. Out beyond the breakwater I counted two small yachts and a trawler, the trawler low on the water and well in towards land.

The dock light at my shoulder was dormant. Last night it had been flashing green as Siôn talked about the past and the people he wanted to keep in touch with when he was cleared. He was wearing the baseball cap I'd bought him to hide his face from passers-by. Being Siôn, he wore it pushed up on his forehead, not hiding his face at all. After the talk, we'd watched a little clinker-built job cut across the flanks of pleasure-craft, pushing and dipping its way out of the harbour on its way to the fishing fields. The single lamp on top of its house, and its oily reflection in the sea, were still visible well after the rest of the boat had vanished, folded into the blackness beyond the roar of the surf.

'What wouldn't I give...' said Siôn.

'A tramp steamer to the Azores,' said I.

'Patagonia,' said Siôn, 'or the Congo...'

'Havana?'

'Cuba, yes! That's it. Join the revolution.'

The Conradian fantasy held until the last minute flicker of light had been extinguished. More breakers smacked against the sea-wall, bursting and tumbling, and the spittle of stars over the long white cliffs grew ever more indistinct. Sea and sky were closing in on us. Siôn didn't move. He was still staring out into the void, his eyes burning in the livid glow of the dock light.

'I'd never leave my girls,' he said, the words uttered for no-one but himself.

I pulled down the peak of his cap and he smiled across at me, the smile spreading over his face as a thick blade of sea-spray enveloped us. The following afternoon, all that was left of the squall was filling in some dimples in the concrete at my feet. A still-high sun beat down from the cloudless sky. Down below, a thirty-footer with red-flashed bows and a windshield cut its engine and drifted in through the harbour mouth, passing a breakwater made up of great lumps of concrete splashed with seaweed like mint sauce. A hefty, shockheaded figure waved at me from the port side of the hull as if he knew me. I waved back, wishing Siôn was with me. So much wishing Siôn was with me.

Back at the flats, I pushed through the solid paintless door and dawdled up the three flights of stairs. I don't like lifts and I wasn't in a hurry. I didn't see anyone - in all the time we were there I only remember seeing two other tenants, and that early on. The stairwell was always airless, no matter what the weather, and silent apart from an occasional tremulous vibration when a hand or knee brushed against the metal bannisters. But when I reached our door, I noticed something different about the silence, something malign. As the key cleaved to the lock, I felt a taut pulsing in my throat; when the door opened from the inside, drawing my weightless hand into the flat, well, right then I knew. Mum met me halfway down the narrow hallway, her eyes raking my face like headlamps, like she wanted to make sure it was really me, that at least one of us would be coming home today. She started making little sideways jabs with flattened palms.

'No,' she said, shaking her head, 'no, no ...'

Dad was on the telephone, his face white and rigid, his eyes dark with weeping, as one of the security men relayed details of the verdict from outside the court. When he put the receiver down, he ventured a hand forward and we embraced, the back of his shirt damp under my palm; then he sank onto the sofa. Mum and I curved dizzily away into the other chairs. In those few minutes, before the telephone calls started rolling in, we sat in a state of abandonment, going over the judge's words: 'Compelling evidence'... 'Life imprisonment'... 'Danger to the community' - each one a grenade to splinter in your brain and tear at your insides.

And then, quite unexpectedly, Siôn rang. He'd been taken to Lewes prison and had been allowed one call. Dad spoke to him first, then Mum, then Dad again, both of them minting fresh hopes on the spot, trying to find a healing phrase which wouldn't wither on their lips, which might yet confound the hour and the knowledge that he was gone from us.

'Llew's here,' said Dad, as if I was a stroke of unforseen good fortune, and handed me the receiver. The voice on the end of the line rose hesitantly, as familiar as my hand but now more distant than ever. I can't remember what he said, but it was the sound of backyards and gardens, of tiny bedrooms and echoing dormitories, of the backs of cars and first days at school. It was a sound which fretted the memory, sharp and at that moment almost painfully moving. When he'd gone, Mum took my hand, and Dad started jotting down some of the things we had to take over to the prison in the morning, his teeth closed on his lower lip, all the loving and struggle in the world transferred to the compiling of a list.

We didn't watch or listen to news broadcasts; we hadn't for a while, having concluded that the media was as important in our lives as we allowed it to be.

In the early days, after Siôn's arrest, I'd scour the news-stands, in the hope of finding, if not good news, then better news, or no news at all. Some hope. As for television, its recurrent tone of flatulent sincerity becomes, in the course of time, as depressing as the venality of the tabloids. Radio is best, the least adulterated. But even the radio stayed off that night.

One of the security men came to see us, looking distraught. As he left, he said: 'I'm really sorry. He was a great guy.' It was good of him to think of us. He didn't have to call round. It wasn't in the contract. *Was* a great guy, though ... actually, it felt pretty accurate. It was a kind of bereavement, after all.

Later on, no food in the flat and ragged with emotion, we decided to go for a bite to eat at the Italian restaurant. A mistake. The shining faces and tinkling laughter all around us only increased our misery and sense of isolation. Just when I thought things couldn't get worse, a dewy-eyed waiter began playing Elton John songs on his accordion, a performance full of elaborate flourishes and hopeless ardour. 'It's no Sacca-rif-fice...' he sang, as I tried to tear an olive off my vulcanized pizza. On another night it might have been funny.

Dad rallied, talking of the way forward, manufacturing confidence, it seemed, with his knife and fork. Mum didn't speak at all, just sat, for the most part enclosed in a coiled immobility, occasionally touching my arm or wadding bits of her napkin with her fingers. Despite personalities as dissimilar as it is possible to imagine, my parents' marriage has endured in a state of deep affection and armed neutrality for more than forty years. It seemed an improbable achievement at times; it did that night, at least for the first part of it. As much as anything else, it was the old question of differences in rhythm and reaction. They were like two people throwing a ball to each other, each fluffing the catches.

Dad had his strategy, his programme for meeting lawyers and planning the appeal; now he had to direct his emotions into a symmetry sufficient to get him through the next few days. More than ever he needed a shared response, a common goal. He sought salvation through order and the reassurance that he was right. But Mum was attuned to none of this. In the hours following the verdict she wasn't looking for a way forward, or a call to arms. She simply wanted to be left alone, to be quiet, to be granted the time to think about Siôn, and miss him, and grieve for him. It was the only response that made any sense to her.

As the meal progressed, Dad grew more frustrated, Mum more defensive. The wheezy inflections of the accordion mocked us and the silences stung. I recall Dad's lowered eyes, the reflected light dying in them as Mum broke down and ran out; the eyes too of strangers watching me as

I went after her, and the jackal teeth of a woman in a patterned top, tugging at her friend's arm so he wouldn't miss the excitement. I found Mum standing in a smear of light by the taxi rank. Her face was trembling and moisture clung to her lashes. As another tuneless dirge struck up, I held her tight, feeling her hot tears on my neck, turning her away from the ogling faces at the restaurant window.

By the time Dad came out, bewilderment crumpling his face, she'd somehow gathered herself. She assembled a smile, of sorts, and his eyes dwelt on her with clumsy devotion. Then he made a dab at her wrist, and she moved under the arch of his arm. Within the terrible hours of that afternoon and evening, that single act of reconciliation stands out as a kind of pinnacle. It might not be a marriage made in heaven, but the character of each has been honed for a lifetime on the other, and their interdependence is more thorough and pervasive than either will ever, generally speaking, acknowledge. Thank God, that night, and before it was too late, they did acknowledge it. That night they'd face their horrors and desolations together. And for now that would be enough.

As we walked back across the marina, the surf reverberating among our thoughts, a breeze rose and Mum found a voice as big as a ball bearing. She said she'd pack Siôn's things in the morning rather than tonight. Dad said that was a good idea, the best thing to do, and we talked again about how well he'd sounded on the 'phone, and wondered if he had his sleeping tablets with him. When we reached the flats, I decided to walk on by myself for a bit. I walked as far as the harbour. Darkness had fallen over everything like a spill of ink. I could barely make out the arc of the sea wall, but heard the voices of anglers drifting across the invisible water, and saw a gull cruising on moss-green wings above the flashing green of the dock light.

That night I slept in Siôn's bedroom. It felt curiously disloyal. On his bedside cabinet sat a comb with his hair in it, some letters from his daughters, Hughes' Tales of Ovid, a Frankie Howerd tape, some wine gums and a prayer printed on a bookmark: Isaiah 41.10, something about 'I will uphold you with my victorious right hand'. I read it, and tried to feel Siôn's thoughts beating in my brain, but couldn't. So I retreated instead into the inchoate hopes of another time, nearly twenty years ago, back when we used to meet on Sunday afternoons, me a student, Siôn a penurious sculptor, pooling our money for coffee and cheesecake at the National Film Theatre.

One Sunday, money gone, we wandered over to Waterloo Bridge and looked eastwards towards St. Paul's and the City, our elbows brushing as the sun sank into the Thames and lights started twinkling on the banks. It must have been winter. We stared down into the swirls of current, holding the silence between us for a good twenty minutes, maybe more, until the gloom to the west brought a chill and we moved on to the tube station. There we parted, without fuss, me to catch a train to Northwick Park, Siôn to walk back along the Embankment on his way to he-didn't-say-where. From high on the station steps, I watched his solitary figure recede into the thickening dusk, and felt a catch at my heart. I knew he'd been sleeping rough; I wondered where he was going, and if anyone there listened to him as I did. I can still smell the damp pavement, see the press of faces going down to the tube. It has at least as much reality as that day in Brighton, the walks to the harbour, that dismal flat.

I lay awake until dawn, tired of hope, tired of thought. Then I switched off the light, which had nothing left to light, and rested for a couple of hours until I heard Dad moving about.

I rocked to and fro, navigating through the wash-day steam like an overladen light aircraft cutting through fog. Ahead of me, on the floor by the sink, was a puddle of sunlight, and I tumbled into it, pitching and rolling against Mum's legs. Scents cajoled into life by an early shower rode in through the door on a bloom of sunshine, mixing with steam in an incense cloud. I looped my arm round Mum's ankle, my head lolled back, and I gazed up at the slim young woman, her pencil skirt barnacled with suds, hauling suety towels out of a tin bath on top of the cooker. They looked delicious and I eyed them hungrily.

Over the years, my memory has distilled the vague chronology of that time down to this: a single wash-day in the early sixties. I'm four, or thereabouts, and my world is still the house where I was born, a Victorian terrace in Brockley, south London, where we - Mum, Dad, my brother and I - lived in two rented rooms and shared a kitchen, bathroom and lavatory with two other families.

That day I was lifted up by carbolic-scented hands and deposited under the kitchen table. From there, submerged beneath burnt oak, I surveyed my clammy domain and traced satisfying shapes upon the surface of the lino, wriggling through a thicket of table legs and chair legs in pursuit of spirals and circles and vanishing elephants. Outside the back door, the sky was a clean clear blue. The lines of a railway track, etched in silver across the mottled mid-distance, flared briefly then faded away, whilst in our concreted yard a line of washing hung slack in the heated air. And below the washing, in a patch of shade by a blistered wall, sat my brother, his legs scrunched up, his face full of careful gravity as he bent a bendy policeman into a variety of improbable poses.

Fifteen months older than I, Siôn had long since eschewed my carpeted paths to tobacco-tinted rooms. Even the warm embrace of the kitchen could no longer hold him. Siôn lived outdoors. Shot through with curiosity and sharp as pepper, he had once, aged three and a bit, famously absconded through a side gate, to be brought home an hour later by the proprietor of a car showroom on Brockley Road. He'd been found sitting in the front seat of a Bentley, gnawing on the steering wheel. After that taste of freedom, the tender entreaties of my mother were fated to fall on deaf ears. Suffused in the wonder of his mind's dream, he stalked the backyard like an emperor in exile, gorging on sun and rain alike, plotting escapes and examining every object with lofty purpose, occasionally smiling to himself as if weighing a secret or two.

Suddenly he stiffened. The toy fell from his hands and he twisted sideways, a Start-Rite sandal tucked under his shorts. Sandy hair foamed over his forehead as he scanned the bank which fell away from our row of terraces. I tilted forward, straining my ears above the *chunka chunka splush* of the twin-tub. From next door came a dead thump like a deflated football hitting concrete. It was followed by a child's howl and a mother's paint-stripping shriek:
'Mar-cel!'

Marcel was whisked indoors. The twin-tub belched to a finish. In the distance a whistle screamed; then a rumble, fattening in the western sky, fell upon my soap-pinked ears and made my skin prickle. Siôn's face broke into a broad grin. As a stinging note loafed up from the railway track, he gave a yell and flew off down the yard, jumping over tussocks of grass, rushing towards the clamour of metal and steam and speed. I turned my face to the table leg, my eyes clamped shut as the goods train crashed through on its way to Lewisham, its throaty roar filling my head like the gargling of a roomful of giants.

A breath of air hit my cheek and cracked my eyes open. The hem of Mum's skirt flicked by, the racketing of the train receding with her footsteps. By the time she reached the larder, the fractured scene had already mended itself. Siôn traipsed back up the yard, hands jammed into pockets, lips moving in thoughtless rumination. Next door a motorcycle coughed, stuttered, throbbed briskly; our larder door, white as melted tallow, squeaked twice. The grasshoppers on the bank started piping. The corner of a sheet flapped in a sneeze of wind. My brother sat down by his patch of wall and resumed his bending of the bendy policeman. The golden world was restored, the train a memory, a ferrous tang caught on the air, an admixture of hot copper and coal smoke.

From the belly of the house came a groan of floorboards and a heavy tread on the stairs. Swallowing gulpily with pleasure, I craned my neck as a pair of heavy boots, loaded with my Dad, crossed the gummy brown floor like tanks over Flanders mud. His laces danced - I lunged at them but missed - chair legs growled on the lino, and a stream of unintelligible words and sentences stuttered into shivers of cutlery, scrapes of crockery and woody creaks. I tracked each note like a hunter, firing shells from my eyes and reloading with a blink, until a metallic screech sent me sprawling.

The oven door hung open like the jawbone of a dragon. The breath it disgorged was warm and meaty; it swam over everything, glazing the windows and making my face glow and my lip sag damply. Scuttling towards Dad's toe-caps, I arrived in time to see the rim of his plate spreading over the edge of the table in a china smile. I gave his trouser leg a couple of tugs. It was like summoning a lift: in a trice I was hoisted up, kissed and folded around his knee.

My heart's desire lay frowsting in a bed of brussels sprouts. I rocked forward and studied its glistening surface with calm approval, then gave it a prod. It dimpled and sent up a little gasp of steam. Before I could move in for another go, I was bounced away from the table into Dad's blue poplin shirt. His police shirt. I didn't know what a policeman was, but I knew he was Very Important, and that the Most Important thing he did was stand outside the Marquis of Granby pub. Sometimes Mum would wheel our twin-pram down there to watch him, a young man in gauntlets the size of pillows, directing the traffic, directing the world I thought, telling it what to do: how the sun should crack the sills outside our room, who got to drink Tizer, who was allowed to have a dog. But he grew weary of it - of the shift work, of the casual violence, of bringing up a family on a copper's pay. So he started applying for other jobs. One was in a flour mill; another was working for Campbell's Soups; the last was a sales job in Michelin Tyres. He got the Michelin one and we moved to South Wales. It's funny, now, thinking of him outside the Marquis of Granby. Funny and kind of sad.

But on that day he was on lates, one till ten, getting ready in bits and pieces, and trying to lean into a forkful of mince roll. I was trying to fish a cigarette out of the pack of Piccadilly in his shirt pocket. Behind me, Mum spoke with a bantering inconsequence:

'... so I went to Carr's, told them I wanted stoned prunes, and Joyce said "stoned, yes, now does that mean *with* stones or without stones?" '

Her cooing laugh mingled with Dad's tinkling forkwork as I launched a cigarette from his pocket to the cleft of his chin. The docking procedure was barely under way before I was returned to the floor like a badly wrapped parcel, my hand holding the cigarette aloft in the manner of the Olympic torch. When this was plucked from my fingers, I cleared my throat and freed a loose-lipped whine. Dad said something in a wry undertone and began fixing a collar to his shirt. Out of nowhere came my Mum's voice, fresh and candid, the unguent of early summers:

'Now then, love ...' she said, cupping her hand under my chin.

Caught in mid-sob I raised a pained eyebrow. Her face was in front of me, finely-boned and lucent. Her biscuity eyes were dusted with gold. She was a most beautiful young woman at that time.

'What's this?' she said, and stuffed something sticky into my fist. I put my pout away and pondered a treacly slab of Harvo malt bread bearing a squash of butter. As the kitchen sounded with indulgent laughter, I beamed across the shafted sunlight, my spirits quite restored, cramming the malt bread into my mouth. My jaws could hardly move and buttery juices trickled under my chin.

In early childhood such renewals occur daily, and in bunches. I accepted each one as easily as I accepted love or censure, for instinct had yet to be fashioned into behaviour. So when I clambered up the kitchen steps into the dimly-lit hallway, and looked about me, everything seemed good, alive with possibilities, and imbued with a pristine freshness. I was extremely pleased with the life I'd found myself in the middle of.

Dad's new bike was filling the corner next to the front door. He'd got it on hire purchase at five shillings a week. I wiped my mouth and wandered over to it across a pasture of green carpet. The OXO tin on the back was open for his sandwiches. I flipped it shut; I gave the pedal a spin and strummed the springs under the saddle; I laced my fingers through the spokes. When I pulled them out the front wheel folded in, something went *chling bing*, and the whole thing crumpled to the floor like a shot antelope. The whirling front wheel ticked crazily. At the same time the dog over the road pulled on its chain and howled. I drew a convulsive breath and inclined my head towards the kitchen. No-one emerged. The drone of subdued muttering went on. Before the front wheel finished revolving, I was nestled behind a stair post, staring at the pile of bike, and taking an almost carnal pleasure in my capacity for destruction.

From far above came a dry, scratchy sound like something being kicked across bare floorboards. I wriggled onto my back, dug my heels into the bottom stair and squinted up through layers of mouldering decoration, following the white bannister rail as it soared upwards like a vapour trail, spiralling on and on into the shrouded mystery of the upper floors. The nape of my neck was pressed hard between my shoulder blades. My brain swam, and through an hallucinatory fug I glimpsed rouged light from the first floor landing dripping over the stairs like plum juice. Above that, the stained-glass panels in the double-doors of my parents' bedroom were ablaze.

It was a call I could not resist. I hitched my calico top into my Ladybird shorts and began the ascent of those steep, irregular stairs, listing right and left, my knees up to my chin, palming the arm-thick bannisters on one side and the rotting surface of chill plaster on the other. Halfway up I heard someone coming down the next flight. With animal instinct I went to ground, my bottom touching the stair just as a swish of liver-coloured suit orbited the stair-post and stopped dead on the landing. It was one of our fellow tenants: a ginger, thin-flanked young man with big teeth. He reared massively above me, his head framed by stained-glass, livid colours smudging his hair. There was an awkward lull, through which I chewed my lip and he dangled a nut-brown brogue over the edge of the landing like a nervous bather testing the water. He did a tusky grin which showed little amusement and might even have held a sketch of enmity: I had once opened the lavatory door on his sitting wife. I remembered her shocked eyes, his caustic voice as he rode to the rescue. I hadn't cared much for the experience either. Now I huddled over my sandals, picking at them and hoping he would go away. But when I looked up his eyes were on me.

'Shouldn't you be outside?' he said, still perched on the landing, still grinning. I just looked, said nothing. The grin began to crumble.

'Sunny day like today,' he added, a nettled tone faintly emergent. Then he took a step forward. His suit was loose, mobile; it seemed to pour itself down the stairs of its own volition. I rolled up into a ball, my knees packing my eye sockets, and started humming. You can do that sort of thing when you're a child. It's one of the perks of the job. But my timing was rotten; I stopped humming just as his brogues hit my stair. The tremor crawled all over me. I felt his distaste like a coat over my shoulders.

Only when the sound of his footsteps had dwindled to nothing did I stop humming a second time; only when I heard the front door close did I unwrap myself and begin climbing again, leaning and lurching, struggling for leverage and breath. At long last, fistfuls of light, gold and green and red, began dappling the wall-side of the stairs. It was like spotting seagulls close to shore. With a windy sigh I dropped onto the last two stairs and hauled my torso into the sanctified glow of the stained-glass. Its variegated patterns were scattered over the threadbare carpet like rose petals on a garden pond. A mood of pure delight overwhelmed me. I splayed my legs, sheathing them in harlequin tights; cross-legged I rocked from side to side, spluttering merrily and watching my shadow rising and falling against the misted wall. On all fours I slunk across the landing like a spice-coated cat, peering hotly through the bannisters.

Next I cast a lubricious eye on my parents' bedroom. I had never been in there alone, not during the day, but now, seized with sudden courage, I nudged the doors open with my face and entered the room's indrawn stillness. A clean-edged rectangle of light was spread out like an altar-cloth before the big bow window, and devotional pictures punctuated the walls: oddly-placed images, picked out in crystal beading, of the Virgin and of Christ in agony.

On a shelf above the bed was a figurine of a horse, up on its hind legs, nostrils flaring, hooves pawing the gilded air. I advanced discreetly to the bottom of the bed and gawped up at it, my chin pressed against a corner of the eiderdown. Eyes other than mine would have deemed the horse utterly innocuous; I alone had comprehended its true nature and purpose, in the dead of night, when the light of a full moon had rimmed its outline and gleamed off the packed muscle and milky expanse of its chest. From my cot I'd heard its dreadful whinny assume the shriek of an oncoming train. I'd watched, massive-eyed, its stamping hooves hover over my Dad's head with murderous intent, whilst headlights played over the crystal-beaded icons, igniting a skein of phosphorescent flashes and lacing the room with primitive magic. It was then, standing up in my cot, a scream caught in my throat, that I'd swept the horse off its shelf and on to my Dad's pillow. It narrowly missed his head.

Now I slipped off the eiderdown and watched as a wave of sunlight climbed up the headboard and burst upon a vista of pink wallpaper. Against this shimmering backdrop, the white horse appeared glassily balanced, almost translucent. But it was, after all, just a china horse. On seeing it again I'd expected to be scared, and I wasn't scared. But I still walked out of the room backwards.

Outside the door I found Siôn, chin tipped into his chest, regarding me solemnly through pale-lashed eyes. Wordlessly we passed each other, and I made the next flight alone, stepping with studied caution into those unhallowed upper reaches. This was uncharted territory. I stood rooted to a little half-landing, sniffing odours of damp wallpaper and listening to the buzzing of a bluebottle. The next staircase was the shortest, only ten or so shallow treads leading to a green-stained door, slightly ajar. The bannisters here were thin and wood-wormy. Halfway up, one trembled in my hand, and once again I sat down. The bluebottle was lying near a brass stair rod - or, rather, its cobwebbed shroud was. It wasn't buzzing anymore. Then it twitched: a death spasm which took it to the top of the stair rod, where it settled for a moment before falling back. Gripped by a ghoulish sense of privilege, I watched it, hardly blinking, until its serenity became burdensome.

The last few stairs were bare wood. They clicked and creaked as I rose into the hot-smelling air of a long narrow room lit by a skylight. A sloping ceiling was crossed by beams swathed in cobwebs, the floorboards were furred with dust, and wallpaper was peeling off the walls in mighty strips. I was not the room's sole occupant. A beetle was weaving determinedly along the line of the skirting board, making a sound like crackling paper. With a whoop I ran over and shadowed its rectangular progress until it got halfway along the short wall. Here, as if tipping the nod at a speakeasy, it gave a cryptic shake of its horns and disappeared under a door that appeared to have been crayoned onto the plaster. There was no frame as such, just a wooden panel with, for a small boy, an impossibly high doorknob.

I fretted awhile, feeling the sting of ambition but unsure of what to do about it. I discovered that by pushing my cheek against the door, and straining on my tiptoes, I could just about graze the underside of the doorknob with my fingertips, but no more. Dejection shouldered its way in. I glowered at the door like a dyspeptic Ali Baba, picturing the gaudy adventures I might have had with the beetle, among treasures that would now remain forever hidden.

Siôn appeared at my shoulder, examining the door, and me, with the same impartial disfavour. He tried the doorknob. Tried it again, hard. Bits of the room moved, the door didn't. Then he began jack-knifing his body, trying to get some purchase on the wall, but I'd lost interest - it wasn't my adventure anymore. So I mooched over to the skylight and stretched out underneath it, letting the sun marble my eyelids. The backs of my thighs were warm against the floorboards. I giggled and made loose, whirlpool gestures with my arms, reaching for anything and talking to myself in bubbling spurts. When the conversation flagged, I squirmed onto my belly and gazed across the amber distance to the door. Siôn had gone.

I scrambled up, advancing in tight little steps along a single floorboard. The door was ajar, by the width of a liquorice stick. I waited some moments, then eased it open a bit more, listening hard as I peered into the shadowy space of a windowless box-room. I could make out a sideboard, some upside-down chairs, a table. More chairs and a coal scuttle. No Siôn. Mystified, I set off in no direction, my surroundings growing less and less familiar by the second. My lonely splendour had vanished like the morning mist. I circled this raftered outpost in the sky and felt only its indifference and smothering silence; I yearned for the kitchen, for its scrapes and gurgles, for its nuzzling certainties and promise of forgiveness. For the first time I'd cast myself adrift from that place of parental reassurance, and I wondered how I would ever get back: I'd travelled so far, and for so long...

Deliverance arrived with a scuff and a grunt. I shot back to the box-room in time to see Siôn's head emerge dustily from behind a crop of chair-legs. 'Shon,' I said. Glowing with affection, I crossed the threshold at last, catching the edge of the door behind me and drawing it to. A chary opener, the

74

door was anything but a reluctant closer; its lockworks clicked home in a whisper as unforgiving as any mousetrap. I heard the flapping of a moth, saw door-shaped light splitting a glass tabletop. That was it as far as seeing was concerned. Siôn pulled me down into a narrow wash of light seeping under the door. His eyes were hooded, the line of his mouth grimly set, but I didn't sense any actual displeasure directed at me. Nor, as the minutes staggered by, did I feel imperilled by our situation *per se*. After another fruitless search for an inside handle, we'd settle back into our low-lit lassitude, more or less resigned to our fate, undoing and doing up each other's sandals, breathing in a heavy damp staleness mixed with furniture polish.

When I heard a steady feminine voice on the other side of the door, I struggled to recognise it. After all, I'd never seen Mum up here. She didn't exist here. And when, a short time later, another voice turned up, this one masculine and sonorous, I was frankly alarmed. I wished they, whoever they were, would go away. Siôn, however, was a study in protean cool; furthermore, he seemed to understand what the voices were going on about. He drew me back from the door, his hands on my shoulders, and I waited for something momentous to happen. A bump happened. The floor shivered, then came a slicing sound like a shovel cutting through peat, followed by a squeal of wood and some dark mutterings. It was a mirthless game, capped by a peculiar twang and a suck of air.

Throat dry with dust, nostrils burning, I watched the door edge back from its frame, wiping in a world of stinging light occupied by two ethereal figures. I blinked and the first quivered into an outline of my Mum. Alongside her, scowling, his hand around the neck of an axe, stood an overalled compost of mechanical smells and stains: the man from the garage over the road.

Unsure of my likely reception and how, exactly, to proceed, I hung back, squinting out from a kind of shy distance. Siôn, however, was on the move, and with a brisk, no-nonsense air, towed me into Mum's waiting arms. Gathered up, brandished aloft and fussed over like a liberated hostage, I pushed my face into Mum's hair, making little submissive noises and monitoring her response with sly sideways glances. When Siôn began picking up scraps of attention, I changed tack again and fomented a sort of overheated *bonhomie*. I hopped around in circles, swiped sunbeams and kissed the garage man's knee, smacking my lips at its petrol flavour.

And then I turned to Siôn. His smoke-green eyes appraised me beadily. I simpered. He hit me. I bawled.

Lewes Prison is a gloomy assemblage of Gothic towers, slated turrets and grey stone walls, fronted by a great nail-studded door with a smaller door inset. As we arrived, three young men were being released. They emerged into the bright morning with all the uneasy pugnacity of youth, punching the air and berating the prison walls. I wondered how long they had been in. Not long, perhaps. One was picked up by a shy, elderly woman who might have been his grandmother; the other two stood around, feinting left hooks and right crosses and talking about pub opening times. One of them kept glancing up and down the road, but nobody came and eventually they drifted away.

The next time the door opened, a horribly polite warder came out and took us to one side. Siôn was okay, but he had been taken to the hospital wing 'for his own safety': apparently another inmate had tried to climb up to his cell, and there had been a lot of shouting and posturing among the younger element. Then we were led away from the visitors' gate to an ante-room, where a kindly ex-serviceman frisked Dad and me, and appraised the contents of our holdall. Hardly anything of what we'd brought was allowed - no clothing [it's provided], no razors [provided], no sleeping pills [or other medication], nothing electrical ['you have to fill in a form'], no chocolate or wine gums [or foodstuffs of any kind - they can be injected with drugs]. With each refusal I felt Mum wince, as if each item thrust back into the carefully prepared bag was a tiny rejection of her.

There was no problem with the books I'd put in - some Fitzgerald, the new Roth.

They took a 3D image of our hands and stamped them with something ultraviolet; then, like uncomprehending tourists in a strange land, we set out across the courtyard with a washed-out young Mum, two children with old faces, and a gang of black-suited lawyers laughing and chattering like rooks. On reaching the main block we climbed some steps, and found a door leading to more steps and a stiff-necked warder. The lawyers went one way; the rest of us were motioned into a waiting room already half-full of women and children. Some were sitting in private silences, gazing at the wall. Others chatted with the easy familiarity of regulars. I sat with the gazers, opposite a photograph of a sniffer dog ['I'm good at my job'] and a blown-up article about a visitor who was put away for smuggling drugs into prison. A real tonic.

Our names were called and we were ushered into the visiting room: an open space where inmates sat at a series of circular veneered tables. Across the blurred noise of kids' laughter and fuss of greetings, I saw Siôn immediately. He was sitting in the far corner, head down, enclosed in a glass-fronted cubicle. It was as poignant a picture of separation as you'll ever see. When we reached him, he looked up with dull interest but didn't leave his chair; the angular bones of cheek and jaw didn't flinch. A warder opened the cubicle door and we jammed into the tiny space, messily clasping bits of Siôn's neck and shoulders. He was wearing blue track suit bottoms and a red sweatshirt about two sizes too small. I arranged myself alongside him on top of a table, my knees around my ears, and Mum and Dad sat in front of us like the down stroke of a 'T'. Then we listened to Dad at his best, as his neat, accurate mind took a few off-cuts from the courtroom floor, and fashioned them into excuses for optimism we could all share until something better came along. It was a subtly persuasive, gritty performance, with much ticking off of points with the fingers of one hand on the fingers of another - and I don't think Siôn heard a single word. His eyes, bloodshot and bagged, stared out through the glass as if plumbing secret possibilities, but there was nothing for him out there, only curiosity, alien and unfriendly. When he spoke - a murmur of assent here, a faint inquiry there - I had the distinct feeling he was addressing his own reflection, as if his mind hadn't quite caught up with events and part of him was back in the other world, the world of the flat, of walks along the sea-wall and of future plans. Only when he talked of his daughters did the present impose itself upon him, ripping a sob from his throat and setting his face in an expression of intense, almost reckless longing.

Too soon we heard the blithe creaking of the door and the warder calling time; again I felt sick at heart

- as I do now writing about it - as we wove back across the visiting room. When we got to the exit, I broke my self-imposed rule and looked back. Siôn was pressed against the wall, palms twisted together, staring straight ahead towards nothing. But he was still Siôn, just Siôn, that's all. Lives change; people don't, not really. It doesn't matter how much you find out about them. He could have been in Brockley, wearing a calico top, and sitting by a patch of blistered wall. I tried to catch his eye but couldn't. The crush of people behind me carried me through the door. And so we left him in that noisome place.

On the way back to Wales we stopped at a motorway service station. There I broke another rule. As Mum and Dad queued for coffee, I skimmed through a rack of newspapers. I'd convinced myself that if I absorbed everything they had to throw right then, I'd be immune to it later, like certain varieties of snake poison. I was wrong; it did me no good at all. I can only think that lack of sleep had begun to blunt the edge of my judgement.

I recollect little else about that day and even less about the next few days. Certain memories I do have are all mixed up with conjecture and bad dreams and probably cannot be relied upon; other stuff isn't in order and I have no appetite for putting it in order. But I do remember walking along the promenade in Aberystwyth, softly crying and thinking about being sixty-five years old, my parents long gone, waiting for Siôn in the grey morning outside a provincial prison. There have been troubled times since then, and who knows what lies ahead, but nothing I experience will ever feel as bad as that.

Part Three

SISAL, SLATE AND CEDAR-WOOD

The brown-painted huts of RAF Padgate, a recruit training station extending perhaps three-quarters of a mile along its eastern edge, stood on the fringe of the northern industrial town of Warrington. In 1955, most of these huts were occupied by motley collections of slightly bewildered young men, freshly conscripted into national service. Over the course of his eight-week stay at Padgate, the conscript would be drilled and yelled at until the philosophy of service life had been swallowed hard, and had slipped, piece by piece, past his quivering Adam's apple.

In all likelihood this would be the first time he'd spent any appreciable period away from home. He was lonely, quite scared, trying not to show it. The friendships he'd make over the next two years might last a lifetime, the memories as indelibly stamped onto his brain as his service number, but in those first weeks it was hard, just hard, as hard as the mattress on the iron bedstead in the draughty hut in which he slept. And as he slept he might dream of home fires, of Saturday nights, of a girl left behind, or of roasting the corporal's bollocks over a slow flame.

Or perhaps, in the autumn of 1955, in the seconds before the orderly corporal's screams tore at the roots of his sleep, he dreamt of the lovely and neat dispenser of tea in the NAAFI canteen.

Megan Stazicker, newly arrived and newly-blonde - she was much taken with Kim Novak at the time - was the most talked-about girl on the station, her smile rewarding and allotted to all, impersonal yet overwhelmingly sweet. Shy, solitary boys gazed at her through the seeping warmth of the canteen, plotting their approaches over thick-handled teacups, while the bolder ones switched from teasing to frankness, striking amorous attitudes across the gleaming silver counter. Her charm glowed amid this wide-eyed and besetting pack: this, together with her obvious commonsense, quickly transformed her into something indispensable at Padgate. Under her hazel glance, the young conscripts' burdens grew lighter, they became fresh again, and awoke in her a natural tenderheartedness. They began to bring her their problems, their letters from home. They even brought their girlfriends and mothers to meet her.

Padgate was not Mum's first posting. That it proved to be her last, and most significant, can be traced to a single encounter. She'd got up early one morning to take a cup of tea to her manageress, a bully whose grey eye moderated from hostility to half-tolerant disdain. Returning to the canteen, she broke her step to look at a row of black-branched trees swaying in the north wind. A handful of dead leaves shivered across the parade ground towards her. It was mid-October, a bright day thinning on the way to winter. She trembled with cold, wrapped her arms around herself, hastened on with plunging strides. On the blurred edge of a shadow, she found her path blocked by a bicycle's front wheel.

'You Welsh, then?' Taff Jenkins, one of the corporals. Clear skin, black hair, his green eyes catching the sun-awakening sky. He deigned to fix them upon her for the best part of five seconds.

'Only on Mam's side,' she said. 'I'm Yorkshire.'

'Good enough. See you later.' A quick smile, a nod, a creak of turning pedals; then, thrown back over his shoulder: 'Save me some cake.'

Her lips parted, but no words came through. She wasn't shy, but she wasn't forward either. Still, as she watched him go, she drew a little breath of pleasure. He was cocksure - all the corporals were - but there was something about him, something elusive that rose into the trees, that murmured and dreamed, free from the urge of gravity; that tumbled with the leaves and lay down with the shadows, just the two of them there, sharing a cold bright morning in October, the day thinning towards winter. She could always be moved by atmosphere.

And as she thought about him, growing more distracted, her heart beating louder and faster, she apprehended that here, at last, was someone who could stabilize her life. He'd enlarge it too, in ways she could barely guess at. The prospect alarmed her, excited her. Later that day, they began exchanging histories in random installments, their sentences floating pleasantly over cups of tea and slabs of Nelson cake.

My maternal grandfather, Thomas Ireland Stazicker, emerges from the mists a haunted figure. The son of a punitive father and sour-faced mother, he left his Cumbrian port town for the Great War in 1915. A sensitive, somewhat dreamy young man, his dreams went bad in ill-fitting khaki, dragging munitions across the muddied wastes and verminous squalor of Loos, the Somme and Arras. He saw the slaughter of the pushes, ate and slept underground with the stench of gangrene, and looked on as petrified boys were shot for cowardice. Above all, Tom Stazicker endured. And when the Armistice came, he threw his medals into a ditch and returned home as embittered as any of his class.

'He was a communist then,' Mum told me, 'or said he was anyway. I used to hear him talking about it to the headmaster; the school was right next to our house. They used to really talk those two. I suppose Mr Masters was the closest Dad got to a friend. He didn't really want friends, just us - Mam most of all.'

His marriage, indeed, proved his salvation and the only stroke of good fortune he would ever have. My grandmother, Dorothy-May, was a slate miner's daughter, a cheerfully industrious, quietly humourous Welsh girl, who helped him absorb his disappointments, never judged him harshly and remained devoted to him to the end. They met while he working as a nurse at what was called, in the 1920s, the West Riding Asylum. It was a job he hated from the start, and one for which this broken witness to the greatest human folly of the century was clearly unsuited. The carrying out of electric shock treatments and other manifestations of early mental health care pulled at his already disordered nerves, and the close proximity of work to home always denied him the anonymity he craved. But jobs were hard to come by, he was a difficult man to place, so he determined to stick at it.

Meanwhile, they began the first half of a family: two daughters, Silwyn and Alice, being followed six years later by a son, Owen. Another daughter, christened Megan after the favourite child of Lloyd George, arrived four years after that, by which time they'd moved to a small village in the heart of the Yorkshire dales. This spread in ages explains why Mum has no memory of the whole family living together under the same roof. The period she remembers best really began during the war years, and by then the two elder girls had left to join the ATS and WAAF respectively.

It isn't difficult to understand why she was her father's favourite. She had her mother's spirit and sense of mischief, and a voluble simplicity which both aroused his protective instincts and was balm to his raging mind. He found her tricks of imagination irresistible, and was proud, if baffled, by her freak talent for drawing and painting. She was also a remarkably pretty girl, though this frightened him on her behalf, associating it as he did with the danger of sin. Accordingly, any displays of girlish vanity, even the wearing of make-up indoors, were instantly quashed, and friendships with boys were discouraged. It would be unfair, however, to picture Tom Stazicker as the unbending patriarch. If his was a largely silent presence, it was also a loving one, and Mum recalls his justice, his undoubted fidelity, and those rare flowerings of good humour on outings to Odsal speedway or to Harry Ramsden's in Leeds:

'I loved Ramsden's. Dad did too, until he saw one of the waitresses spitting on a tea towel. We never went back after that. He had a thing about hygiene. They'd call it a phobia these days. We knew it had to do with the war: his war, the first war. He hardly ever came on holiday with us, but when did he took his own towels with him, even to B&Bs, and he'd sleep on top of the bed, never in it. And pork - wouldn't touch it. Pigs, you see, they reminded him of the muck in the trenches.'

Always, then, the demons in attendance. Always the soul groping blindly out into the infinite towards the light. And when it all got too much, when the days were too long and the desolations too deep,

Tom Stazicker would clean shoes. And on those occasions, as she climbed the stairs to bed, Mum would look down and see him among the shoes and brushes and tins of Cherry Blossom, his strong forearm working the brush, his eyes concentrated on the shine of leather. The following morning, every pair of shoes in the house would be gleaming and placed neatly under the dresser.

Mum went on: 'He was a shy man. Liked to go for long walks with the dogs, and fishing down by the canal. Always by himself. Other than that he wanted to be at home. He had this evil-smelling tobacco - 'twist' it was called, like a long tube of tar. I used to cut bits off for him with his penknife, and he'd sit and smoke and read the *Yorkshire Post* classifieds. He was fanatical about the classifieds. Got his shoes through them, and mine - WAAF ones - and a taffeta dress for my birthday. Opening the parcel, you'd never know what to expect. Whatever it was never looked like it was meant to, like it was in the paper. He got one of the first Biros through the classifieds. Just looked like a poor fountain pen to me. Oh, and there was the hairdressing kit: "Why'd you blummin'-well get that, Tom?" Mam said. "It'll come in," he said. It was always "It'll come in" with Dad.

'He was keen on the radio, 'specially when the boxing was on. And he'd listen to the news really quiet during the war. "The Russians'll win it," he'd say; "they're all six foot tall, with white wellington boots."

He thought they were wonderful, the Russians. Never could be doing with the local gentry, though, or anybody that got above themselves. "Swanking" he called it. That's why he hated the idea of Mam being in service. That, and the fact that she was away all the time. He was always jumpy until she got home. But she had to do something. We couldn't survive on Dad's wage. So she did for two of the big houses - cooking, cleaning and suchlike. Even Dad did a bit of gardening twice a week, but we weren't allowed to talk about that. Mam, though, she enjoyed it. All her friends worked below stairs, and everyone liked her, and she could have a laugh. She liked a laugh.'

Tom Stazicker was never less than a serious man.

The people and customs she observed in those houses made a distinct impression on my own Mum. Through them she glimpsed a different kind of life, one which fed her imagination and even suggested distant possibilities. And, of course, there was Hollybank - Doctor Edgeley's house. She liked the Doctor, with his vague smiles and strange, half-uttered confidences. Liked Mrs Edgeley too, all booming and bosomy, tightly-packed in tweed: 'proper gentry' Dorothy-May called her [Tom gave his *Yorkshire Post* an emphatic rustle]. One morning in the dead of winter she gave Mum a necklace, an amber one: 'proper quality'. She has it still.

But the most important thing about the Edgeleys was Hollybank, and those shadowy evenings by the wood-fire, Dorothy-May knitting and chatting with Maud, her best friend, and my Mum loving being there, the kitchen being so big and comforting, and nothing ever changing. Only it did, of course, it did change. All gone now, those direct and trusting faces. The house too. They built flats...

When talking of it, she is borne along a deep-hedged lane towards a Georgian manor-house, with Victorian graftings, tucked away in a cup of land and surrounded by lawns, orchards and a nursery garden. From the hot light outside, she passes through an aroma of mellowing apples into the cool, bright spaces of a kitchen. Sprigs of lavender are drying out on a whitewashed sill. This, then, is Megan's special place of clustered warmth and holy charm, where nothing bad ever happens. Outside the kitchen sits a dresser, hung with pewter plates like the eyes of a Tinder Box dog. It gazes out on a glowing heartland of oak-panelled rooms, each with its own air and sky. In the efficient hush of the study, pavilions of books scale walls the colour of old gold, the upper tiers blending with dark shelves and gradually becoming invisible, while above and about the fireplace hang oil paintings of an unrepentantly English nature, mostly of dogs and dead game birds, lavishly framed. If the Doctor's away, Mum risks a peek. If not, never.

But there's still the dark-blue plain of carpet to skip around, or sashay across like Rita Hayworth, and a stairway twisting and untwisting to upper chambers monopolized by Oriental rugs, wall tapestries and brocaded cushions, fatly stuffed. And, of course, there's the kitchen...

Maud the housemaid, garrulous and bold and a slapdash cook, is busy over bubbling pots, stirring one, shaking another, giving a sensational account of her day off in Bradford. Madge, the gardener's daughter, stands by the silent kettle, a study in boneless lethergy. Her father's billycan hangs loosely at her side. The genial angular Bilton, immaculate in his chauffeur's uniform, sits at the pine table and pops freshly-picked peas into his mouth from an oyster-coloured colander. His snow-white hair is touched by the sun. Who would guess at his other life, as one half of 'The Whistlers'? - they perform at church halls all over West Riding, he singing in a reedy tenor, his wife whistling accompaniment. Each of these remains in Mum's memory as she saw them that day, and more particularly as she left them the following autumn: as the heroes of their own lives, each easing into the others' quietude and becoming faint and unreal in the evening's smoky light.

That was the year Tom Stazicker vowed never to go back to the hospital again. He'd been there more than twenty years, the two elder girls were off his hands, and he'd had enough. There followed a variety of menial jobs, each started in a glow of enthusiasm which quickly ebbed away. He even tried earning a living with his hairdressing kit, biking all over the dales to cut farmers' hair. Alas, the farmers resented paying a bob every two months, so would instruct him to give them shorter and shorter haircuts. It was never going to work out. This latest disappointment proved the final straw. After much solitary walking and smoking of twist, he decided to forge a new beginning: they'd move to north Wales, near to where my grandmother was brought up. They'd buy a house and take in lodgers.

Dawn had broken on 30 December 1951 as Tom returned home from his nightwatchman's job at Prestatyn holiday camp, cycling the eight miles along the coast roads and beaches. It was bitterly cold; the air was heavy and chilled the lungs. My Mum remembers waking around six o'clock, and through a drowse of sleep hearing: 'Shall I get a doctor, Tom? Tom, shall I, shall I get a doctor?' coming from downstairs; then looking through the bannisters and seeing her ailing father, his eyes uncomprehending, clutching his chest. By the time Mum got to him, his head was cradled in Dorothy-May's arms. She was imploring him quietly, insistently: 'Don't leave me, Tom, don't leave me.' Her strong body shook with each sob. She looked up, saw Mum, and in single shocked breath whispered: 'Megan, go get the doctor.'

The nearest telephone box was on the corner by the Co-op. Mum ran down there still in her nightdress, feeling the frosted ground beneath her bare feet, a kind of suffocation in her throat. There were moments of blind panic when she thought she'd forgotten the number, but at last she managed to get through. Already, though, it was too late. When she arrived home, winded and shivering, her father's lips were pale and lifted, his eyes empty, his dreams of a better future ended. The waiting for his other life to catch up with him, his younger life, left behind with the best of his generation amid the dried-out battlefields of France, was finally over. He'd made it home, though. He'd made it home again.

After two days of crying, the family began taking down the Christmas decorations Tom had put up. Then, on the first day of 1952, Dorothy-May brought out a linen tablecloth and began embroidering it. Her face was resolved, composed; there would be no more tears. She had loved this singular, brooding man; had guided and protected him where possible, had taken her gift for living and used it in every way she could think of to make him happy. She had listened to his umpteen schemes fondly and without complaint. Now, in the wakening of a new year, and in the immense silence, she prepared to go on alone.

My own Mum was fifteen when Tom died. For a while she hid from her memories of him, but the consequences of his life, while hardly momentous, had already imprinted themselves clearly on her character. She could not be tempted into sociability, but was kind and loyal to the friends she made, and, of course, fiercely devoted to family. Her sense of wonder, which has only latterly begun to desert her, was born in the atmosphere of love and protection her parents created. This manifested itself early on in her fondness for birds and flowers; in the pencil drawings, dried leaves and cuttings from *Picturegoer* preserved in bulging scrapbooks; and in shoeboxes full of buttons, bits of costume jewellery, and scraps of silk and organza donated by the mistresses of the big houses.

Tom Stazicker's pessimism is his daughter's; as well, she is abnormally inclined to caution, and her willingness to endure can lead to obstinacy, so that views, once uttered, instantly become positions to be defended. But if these are failings, they're as nothing, I believe, when set alongside the purity of her love, the force of her sincerity, and an instinct for natural justice in a personality which, finally, will not accept much domination of any kind.

The day after Dorothy-May began embroidering her tablecloth, the manager of the Co-op where Mum worked told her to take the week off. 'He was a nice man - a champion dancer, you know. You'd see him sometimes after work, quiet, by himself, practising his steps in the warehouse, scattering salt on the floorboards as he danced around. The other girls said I was his favourite - I don't know why.' They would always be drawn to her: the lonely dreamers, the outsiders, the square pegs and dancers across warehouse floors. And she to them. Or, as her future husband would say: 'Why does your mother always like the oddballs?'

She did not remain long at the Co-op, but spent several odd years falling into jobs and dreams of other things. She became a cinema usherette: 'When the spotlights came on - you know, at the ends of the aisles - I could never get down there in time with me ice-creams. I'd have to really leg it...' She even won a beauty contest in Blackpool. Then, desperate to leave north Wales, she got a job serving tea to national servicemen in NAAFI canteens in the north of England. And at one of these she met her young Welsh corporal.

Early light slants through the patterned curtains and stripes the red-bobbled valance on Mam's feather-filled bed. The blankets rise and fall to the sounds of her steady breathing. Everything else hangs suspended in the murmurs of a Spring morning. At the top of her rounded edge is a shock of russet hair, beyond that the motionless hump of Auntie Bet.

In her own bed under the window, thirteen-year-old Megan curls around her pillow, the back of her hand across her eyes to bear the sun. She hears a thump from the attic room: Dad and Owen have slept up there since Auntie Bet came to stay. Turning over, she unwinds, stretches out, yawns. Staring up at the damp-stained ceiling, she listens to the gobbling of chickens in the backyard until Dad's heavy tread sounds on the stairs. There's a chill in the air; she gives a shiver as she tiptoes across the floorboards. She pulls on her red gingham dress and white socks. She pushes her feet into her WAAF shoes, pulls a brush through her hair and goes downstairs.

Tom Stazicker is kneeling down before the hearth, trying to get a fire going. He's holding the *Yorkshire Post* in front of it, cocking his head to read about Bill Bowes bowling out Surrey as the damp coal crackles.

'All right, Dad?'

'Mind me leg, love.'

He's a rangy man in his early fifties, collarless this morning in a coarse shirt, thick grey trousers and waistcoat. His careworn eyes follow his daughter to the corner sink. She splashes herself with water and brushes her teeth, moonishly watching the rivulets of Euthymol toothpaste stream pinkly down the draining board. Tom's frying pan is already spitting behind her: in go the sausages, the potato masher pressing down *tsssh* on fried bread. A packet of Force and the pitcher of milk are already on the table.

Megan sits down, observing her reflection in the glass-fronted dresser. Still dreamy with sleep, she flicks her hair and cocks her chin: she's Rita Hayworth; no, she's Miss Varley. Miss Varley is her

97

favourite teacher. Miss Varley is gorgeous: clear-skinned, gentle, with heavy red hair. Not like Miss Jennings, with her hard little body and her hair scraped into a bun. Miss Jennings slapped her on the back of the thigh for giggling in netball practice.

In comes Owen, hands in pockets, yawning: 'Dad, our Megan's looking at herself again.' He's straight out of the door into the backyard, heading for his Dad's BSA Bantam. Motorbikes are more important than breakfast. A flame leaps from the kindling; a ball of smoke rolls over the mantelpiece. Tranquil intimacy falls again across the room. It comes from the fire, yes, and from the hiss of cooking in the deep listening silence. Megan begins to talk quietly, scraping her heels across the sisal matting. Tom cocks an ear, saying nothing, occasionally nodding. Megan is glad she got up early. She feels quite sure her life will always be this way.

Cardiganshire, latterly Ceredigion, is the maritime and agricultural county of South West Wales: a land of watchful hills and fertile valleys, of fast-running rivers and great blackening skies, and of rain and rising mists over the Tregaron bog. The farmhouses and grey-stone cottages of my Dad's boyhood are still there; the wet slated roofs still glisten as the sun settles behind a square towered church. And still, when the east wind bites hard, chair legs scrape on slate floors, the shadows swell on whitewashed walls, and firelight flickers across china-laden Welsh dressers. On the wall you'll see a picture of an old Welshwoman at chapel, passing pews of cedar-wood; and the sharp-eyed, or the guilty, will see the devil grinning in her shawl. Later, when you're ready for bed, and putting the guard on the fire, you'll hear the snarl of a polecat from the upper end of the valley.

But times have changed. Many of the smaller villages are dying. The young leave for university or for jobs in the towns and cities, and do not return. Fewer and fewer men are needed to work on the farms. The villages are left to a diminishing number of elderly, and to the newcomers, who dabble in arts and crafts, talk of authenticity and restoration, and four-wheel drive to Safeway for the weekly shop. Afterwards, one supposes, it's a decaf and a browse through *Country Living*. Nothing wrong with any of this *per se*, but something precious is lost, you feel. And as past certainties fade, the old ones passively dissent - very Welsh, that - and mutter darkly about being the last of their time. As, indeed, they are. Theirs are the ancient rhythms of rural life; their words run back along lanes innocent of cars, across farmyards and fields that knew the pull of the yoke, the cut of the scythe and the ring of a blacksmith's hammer. On Sundays their voices rose in chapels a-quiver with Christian exultation, *Calon Lân* oozing around the rafters, not a space on the pews to be had. Now, as the lorries from the quarry rumble by, the black kettle simmers, the cat curls in front of the fire, and rheumy eyes scan the obituary columns of the *Cambrian News*.

Take a road roughly south east of Aberystwyth and you'll pass through a number of such villages. One of them will be Ystrad Meurig, where my Dad grew up and where my grandmother lived until her death last year. A bit further on is Pontrhydfendigaid, which is bigger and a bit livelier, and where my grandfather was born. Bear left and you'll arrive at Strata Florida, where he's buried. The small, neat church pins down an expanse of sloping ground divided by a drystone wall. On one side of the wall is a 12th Century Cistercian Abbey, or at least the remains of it: an archway, a few foundation stones, a shaft where they say wine was cooled, some stables and a floor of intricately carved tiles. The Abbey attracts some visitors in summer, but not many - certainly no more than turn up to tend the graves in the churchyard. All those graves, platoons of them. So much marble. I knew a sculptor once, who carved wood most of the time. He said working in marble made him cry.

Anyway, Grandad's at the bottom end, in a turfy section a few rows back from Uncle Goff, his brother-in-law, who used to run Ystrad Meurig Post Office. Uncle John the Pipes is at the top end, along with others of a vintage unknown to me. And above them all, near the church's west door, sits a whacking obelisk in black marble, topped by an eternal flame: the final resting place of Sir David James. From this prime spot, the great philanthropist can cast his eye over those less favoured, and still contemplate as pleasant a prospect of his native land as could be wished for. With him is Lady James, whose image is recalled in one of the church's stained glass windows. It was installed on Sir David's instructions, shortly after his death. A better Christian than I might deem this borderline blasphemous. I'll consider it a forgivable piece of bad taste; he was old; he'd loved and esteemed his wife; he missed her.

Like so many of the Welsh rural poor, Sir David's father had gone up to London in the mid-nineteenth century to be a cowkeeper. In those days there were dairy herds all over the city, supplying their local populations with milk. When Mr James hit upon the idea of using the barley grain discarded by brewers to feed his cows, then selling on the surplus to other cowkeepers, the seeds of his son's fortune were sown. This grew steadily through the nineteen twenties and thirties, by which time my Grandad, Charles Jenkins, had left Pontrhydfendigaid to join Sir David in London. In recruiting young Charlie from his home village, Sir David was typically shrewd; his apparent beneficence repaid in a lifetime of hard-pressed loyalty, long hours and wrecked nerves. Grandad began as a clerk. At the time of his death in 1969 he had become Chairman. And in all that while, his service to James & Son was only interrupted by the outbreak of the Second World War. In 1939 he packed his young family off to Wales, joined the Royal Artillery, and, apart from one or two fugitive visits, disappeared from their lives for six years.

On top of my piano is a yellowing photograph from that time. It shows Pendre, the family cottage in Ystrad Meurig, which they shared with Uncle John the Pipes, the village carpenter and wheelwright, in his sixties even then. The cottage looked very different in those years, chill and squat and roughly finished. A sun-glowing patch is rising up the limewashed stonework. My grandmother, Mary Jenkins, is framed in the doorway. She cuts an impressive figure, her features too strong for beauty, but full of tender authority; and in her eyes a real shrewdness resides. The reflected sun is falling across her shoulder onto the flaxen head of Anne, my Dad's sister. Anne's gaze is bright and confident, her adult trials as yet unglimpsed - is there any silence, I wonder, which reverberates as poignantly as that in photographs? Standing in the foreground is John, the eldest child. He's in shorts and socks, his school cap pushed away from an extravagant fringe. His expression is frank and engaging. Others in the photograph I can't identify; weathered, bucolic faces staring out at me from an irrevocable universe. But everyone is smiling, more or less happy to have their picture taken.

Apart, that is, from young Dai. My Dad.

He's four years old or thereabouts, squirming from his mother's grasp and glaring along the line of children like an affronted cherub; small fists clenched, cheeks blazing, fighting for his due. His world begins with a dirt road snaking up from the village, ends among the thin, waving grass on the edge of an escarpment. Within it he travels watchfully, and he travels alone. Not for him the liberating grandeur of the firstborn. In the candle-guttering dark, between great roars of talk and obscure silence, the thought has already insinuated itself - oh, bitter, bitter knowledge! - that he will never be the favourite. Nor will he, by the end of the war, be the youngest. A little sister will arrive, prettiest adornment so far of this cramped, time-hung gallery, nudging him still further into the shadows. Ahead of him, despite all his fine endeavour, lies greater uncertainty, more mistimed gestures.

The first time I saw the photograph I was sitting alongside my grandmother in the cottage in Ystrad Meurig. It was late afternoon, coming on to early evening, and I was anxious to get back to Aberystwyth before dark. The photograph was one of a pile stowed away in a shoebox. Every so often Nanna'd pluck one out of the box and pass it to me across the biscuits and tea cups, talking of the photograph and of other times, and of other photographs she hadn't passed to me. Three bars of an electric fire were burning. The room was airless and I felt dopey, nearly falling asleep but wanting to show interest.

'Now, here's one...'

I held it between my thumb and forefinger, bringing it in from arm's length. Still the image was fuzzy, so I sat up, patted a yawn and angled the photograph upon my knee. Nanna's softly modulated voice sank a note lower. It was then, as I strained my eyes, that the scene within the snapshot's curling corners hollowed out like the bowl of a spoon, and upon its rolling echoes were carried other sounds, half-heard but wholly understood: the panting of a sheepdog in Tandre, its tongue lolling onto cool slate; the splash of a vole behind the *gweithdy*, distant shoutings to dogs, a parched cry, and the rumbling of sheeps' hooves on the eastern flank of Fflwrwd: each of these interspersed with the creak of old oaken planks and the mute image of my Dad's hands, white against the dark, loamy earth, pushing Huw Bronllan's raincoat down a rabbit hole. The earth oozed back through his outstretched fingers. And in all of this there is an intensity of feeling, a distinct tone, compounded of things I'd known or seen myself, or been told about, or that had reached me balanced on the edge of dreams, stillborn and whole...

SISAL, SLATE AND CEDAR-WOOD

At Strata Florida station, a lantern's glow is reflected in a stagnant pool of water. John Tandre is loading mailbags on to a furiously hissing locomotive. Two boys are with him, both nine or ten, both bundled-up against a biting wind. My Dad, hot-faced with effort, makes a bright shape against the curve of the engine, exhaling white breaths under a flop of black hair. Moc, his best friend, is taller, all forehead and nose and wheezy giggles. For him, a lonely suicide at forty, life will never again seem so simple and so good. This day he has an eye to the manner of the job he's doing, lifting the mailbag first on to his knee, then hoisting it into the guard's red hands. There's a sting of frost on the air; tents of steam freeze before opening on to the wilderness of Tregaron bog. Through a long whistle of steam, doors slam, shouts ring out from the footplate, piston rods shudder, and the train slides away from this tiny outpost of GWR, running quieter than a river through the purple dusk, headed for Caradog Falls Halt, for Trawscoed, for Llanilar, Felin Dyffren Halt, Llanrhystyd Road and Aberystwyth. The boys chase each other home past the Post Office, running through a miry gateway, Moc's forearms loosely lifted. Back in the office, John Tandre books in some luggage from the guard's van. An oil lamp burns at his back, illuminating a patch of Canadian pine and columns of tickets the colours of barley sugar.

As the mountains recede behind a chilling mist,

the sun sinks in shades of pink and gold and milky grey. The station lantern starts to swing, gently to and fro, its creak pitched on a rising wind. A tuft of wool, caught on a sprig of gorse, twitches, is released, flies upwards, upwards, banking and eddying on a north easterly, alighting on the bank above Uncle Arnold's, where the whitening bones of a raven rattle in the fork of a lightning-struck ash.

This house, Froneithinog, is squarishly severe, is girded by tall pines and clings to a hill outside Ysbyty Ystwyth. Here, on the higher ground, winter breezes have already bitten. The earth is blackened and crusted. Not far away, at Teifi Pools, where the red kites cloudily wheel, hill farmers are breaking ice for the beasts' drink; and a flurry of snow has held on the Cambrian mountains, now oozing across the eastern horizon like dusted marzipan.

Uncle Arnold, cadaverous, brown-suited, sits alone in a lofty bare room, mistily engaged in bits of mental arithmetic. I can hear his silence, his short changes of breath. A bead of moisture struggles down the side of his nose. A fire is burning in the wide hearth, burning low, with a deep glow from the heart of the embers, and now and then a leap of blaze. The room has two windows, both small and grimy; smells of earth and closeness seep from its walls and the stone-flagged floor. There is an absence of hope in this room. Arnold is Mary Jenkins' cleverest uncle: an accountant, Swanseaeducated no less, a Reader at church on Sundays. Deafness and the loss of his voice exhausted his finances and ended his prospects. Blindness broke his heart. He has a clock with the face removed, allowing him to trace the position of the hands, but time means little to Uncle Arnold.

Mary visits him often, tapping her messages expertly onto the back of his hand. At the sudden recognition he smiles sweetly, his eyes blink in a kind of thankful rapture, and he sits forward, poised on the balls of his feet. The logs are prodded, the fire grows warmer on his hands and face, and one of Mary's children, usually Dai, kisses his sunken cheek. He feels their love, close and unpitying, throughout the day, until the fire has died and its ashes are cold in the grate. Alone again, he sits back, his delicate fingers drumming out figures and combinations of figures on the arms of his chair, a quality of repudiation flickering in his dead eyes.

In Ystrad Meurig a boy is leading his cart homeward. His boots are covered with great slabs of muck. The horse coughs; its matted flanks heave as the cart creaks up the hill towards Penygraig Uchaf. The day declines like a drowsy eyelid, its fractured sun settling over hills and fields, distance and vista, bathing everything in its soft transfiguring light. Before the last jangle and tramp have died into silence, cart and horse and boy have become a single silhouette against the restless sky.

CALICO BOYS

This silence, for a moment, seizes all things.

The door of the *gweithdy* creaks open, and Uncle John the Pipes, a powder of wood-dust on his forearms and beard stubble, comes out and breathes in the honey-smell of centuries. Heavy shadows are flooding the valley. With a certain sense of relaxation, the old wheelwright cradles the bowl of his pipe and scratches under his cap-band. The evening has a beauty about it now. Lamps are lit in College Arms, in Tandre and Bronllan. A train huffs down the track from Aberystwyth, its plume of steam no more than a smudge on the gently undulating air.

The night comes on blue-black and wintry; flakes of snow feather the casements of Ystrad Meurig, piling high on sills and ledges and on the leafless branches of trees. In Pendre, the air is thick and palpitant, and sleepy-cat warm. Amid the din and swirl of children's faces, a pot of rabbit stew is bubbling, wrapping them all, John and Dai, Anne and baby sister, in a succulent fog. Uncle John shifts his legs from under the settle, his ears red, his gaze sweeping the room above a triangle of grey neckerchief. He nods once, leans forward and spits on the fire. The children follow the phlegm's trajectory, in thrall to stray gobbets fizzing on the hearthstone.

Later, within the full-fed and glowing sprawl of her family, Mary eases her tired body on to the settle. She gives a long sigh, letting go of toil, and listens to the wireless until the wet batteries falter.

Playing cards are rooted out; everyone plays, clapping down and picking up, the scrapes and laughter lingering across forgotten time. They linger still as Mary reads aloud her absent husband's letter from the war. When her voice drifts away, on an indefinite note, the children's expressions at last grow speculative and intent, their eyes searching for the stranger, Daddy, in the red and blue-blocked floor.

Towards bedtime, as firelight shrinks the room with shadows, its flushed spaces are filled by a succession of callers: shadowy paragons these, exhumed from scratches of memory: the Miss Lloyds, light-voiced, bearing their round pat of butter; Johnny Maesbynadlog, his fist pressed to his cheek, a faint uneasy smile upon his lips; Ellis Tandre, inscrutably placid; Moc Bryn Teifi, Tom Williams, and John Tandre, up from the station, his face carrying its peculiar luminosity, a thin ironical smile playing around his lips. They've come to order carts or cartwheels, or coffins, or to settle accounts - or perhaps, drawn to his commanding presence, for Uncle John's counsel. As well, on nights like these, a tale or two might be traded: portent-laden, darkly elliptical, possessing inferences of paganism, born of superstition, vast silences and unlit roads.

All breathed the air of this place, appeared eternal, and were gone in the white glint of an unblinking eye, their lives seeming not to end, but to vanish: they who worked hard, committed little harm, followed the imperatives of family and performed their simple deeds of affection and faith. They leave tonight under a pink moon, the village gleaming white under snow, disappearing one by one as the shape of the church casts its giant shadow across their path. And in the biding dreamy aftermath, as wainscots snap and talk languishes, young Dai dozes between his mother and Uncle John, chased into sleep on a slowly withdrawing tide of voices.

War ended and bells rang out across the sheep-cropped hills. For many, the peace was ushered in virtually unnoticed, the years of conflict having barely registered a tremor on the calm surface of rural life. For others, such as my Dad, it changed everything. First his father returned to the family, upsetting a delicate internal machinery tuned over six years of independence; then, almost before he knew it, they were all back in London. Always the least secure of the children, too-young too-old, often painfully sensitive, he now found himself an exile in a foreign land. At his Grammar school, savvy London kids mocked him mercilessly for his heavy Welsh accent, and to walk the streets was to be assailed by the unfamiliar: endless rows of houses, teeming bodies, traffic and mercantile clamour. Eventually, of course, with the aptitude all children have for accepting whatever - good or bad - is granted to them, he started to make the best of it, and even got caught up in new freedoms. But fifty-odd years later, when I asked him about that time, the kids' taunts still resonated, not as words but as something for eyes to hear, and I could see him returning to the basement flat in bombed-about New Cross, choking on the silted air, feeling out of step and lonely, and longing for shining fields and gentle faces.

At sixteen he was an unhappy clerk in the City; at eighteen he was called up for his National Service. He shone. He found parts of service life unpleasant, but by no means all, and he responded well to its contradictions: to its diversity and cohesion, to its restricted version of democracy. The experience of being away from home, thrown on to his own resources, relieved him of a burden he had not properly realised was there. He opened up, made mates he'd never forget, did everything that was asked of him, and did it well. After twenty weeks he was made corporal. Still only nineteen, he was posted to RAF Padgate, drilling upwards of one hundred and twenty men at a time. He soon discovered that it wasn't the officer class, but the sergeants and corporals, bright working-class boys like himself, that made the whole thing work. After three and a half years in the RAF - he'd signed on for an extra year - he felt new, strong, and shorn of respect for the social prohibitions in which British life indulged. And, of course, my Mum was with him. They'd found many things in common, and even more on which to disagree; the sum of both bound them together. So their worlds shifted, changed, danced on.

In many ways he is very Welsh. Ever prey to melancholy and the needlings of an unquiet mind, he's always, in his baffled quest for himself, been able to rely on his tremendous self-discipline to win him breathing space. In this space he'll often communicate more in silence than in words, but there's always a willingness of the heart: to believe in himself, and in a better future, where he will do even better, and be loved even more for it. Therein lies his redemption, and mine too, in a way. I remember the time - I would have been fifteen or so - I ran away from home. Some run. That year we were stuck in one of the more depressing notches of the stockbroker belt. I got as far as a YMCA near Tottenham Court Road, and hitched straight back home. I remember walking through the door. I heard Dad before I saw him, somewhere back of the house, crying hoarse, hacking sobs, coming from the kind of pain only strong people can feel. And when he put his eyes on me, I had complete knowledge, for the first time, of his love for me. Everyone ought to have a moment like that. Sitting down on the settee later, with his arm around me, both proud of each other, exhausted with emotion - well, if the roof'd caved in, I'd have died happy.

It changed me, I think.

Part Four

GAOL TOWN

I wake around five, knowing something's wrong. How I don't know. Switch on the light and check the alarm clock. It's set it for 6.41 pm, not am. I'd have slept right through. The thought scares any more sleep away, so I get up, make a cup of tea. The kitchen's freezing; the boiler packed up again last week. I put my biggest jumper on over my pajamas and curl up on the sofa, drinking my tea. I look out of the window, out across the Waveney valley. The rain has stopped and a stain of sunrise is glimmering in the flooded fields. The bend in the road is under water, but I should be all right. I take a long bath, just lying there, listening to the radio. I was in the bath, listening to the radio, when I heard that a girl had been murdered in Hastings. That was four years ago, almost to the day. I can't remember exactly how I felt. I'd have thought about Siôn and Lois, of course, and the girls, but it would have been just another news story, a bit more interesting than most because of Hastings. Auden said it in 'Musée des Beaux Arts': "how everything turns away/quite leisurely from the disaster". I think it was the following morning my Dad rang, telling me it was Billie. That's when it all changed, all our lives, forever. I take another look in my satchel-case,

113

checking everything is there, passport too. They need that sometimes.

I reach the outskirts of Norwich around ten past eight. The traffic isn't too bad. Only one hold-up, crawling behind a flock of sheep, the farmer staring back at me with quintessential enmity. But no problem. Plenty of time. I catch the beginning of the morning rush hour, but reach the car park with forty minutes to spare. One time I was stuck in traffic ten minutes before the train was due to leave. I remember the sheer panic, the wild thoughts of leaving the car by the side of the road and running the rest of the way. Never again: I'd prefer to leave at dawn. At the station I grab a coffee and a Danish and wander up to the screens to watch for the Liverpool train. Hang on. The 10.03's up - what about the 9.03? What have they done with the 9.03? I intercept a uniform, pulse galloping. He takes his time, checks his watch, but it's all right: the 9.03's standing at platform six. Okay then. Breathe again. I throw away half the Danish and take the coffee on to the train.

'I'm visiting my daughter,' says the lady - there's no other word - who sits beside me. 'Could you..?' I lift her suitcase up on to the rack. Her face is shaped like an inverted cone. My smile is thin, sour at the edges, but she wants to talk, and I'll do, and she does, all the way to Peterborough. Her voice follows the chuntering rhythm of the train on the track -

lurching, squealing, rumbling along. Her daughter's had a baby, that's all that sticks. At one point I reckon she'll need a nod or something, like fuel, so turn towards her. Turns out she's been speaking to a man across the aisle all the time. He takes her case down at Peterborough, making a big deal of it. She gives him a queenly smile, me a dirty look. I feel some guilt, but not much. Days like this are different, and I'm different in them.

A pale young man in a black suit takes her seat. He smacks an Andy McNab paperback down on the table. We're through Peterborough when the train stops. Just stops. Five minutes pass and the engines shudder down. My eyes rest on a landscape studded with portakabins, pools of rainwater, general railway detritus. Silence. A mobile plays a moronic little tune. A woman laughs, and another helps her laugh; this primes smiles all round. Each second tears at my nerves. Fifteen minutes to make my connection. The pale young man checks his watch, glances over my shoulder. I try and hold his eyes; I want someone to complain with, but he's not interested. Opposite me, a French woman and an American man are poring over a laptop, their talk irrigated with the incomprehensible language of the stock market. More mobiles start trilling. An announcement comes over the address system. It's nothing about the delay, just a grisly welcome 'on behalf of the on-board team'. Bollocks. My vision is getting fogged.

I'm seeing Siôn sitting at an empty table in the visitors' room, with other people, other prisoners and visitors, sneaking glances at him, shaking their heads. I'm working on the possibility of jumping out and running back to Peterborough station when the engines start throbbing and we're on our way again. The tension bleeds away. I glance down at the pale man's book. Wonder how good ol' Andy would cope with all of this. I spiral off into a fantasy where Andy McNab leads a team of commandos and breaks Siôn out of Wakefield. Genuinely, I do. No light-heartedness here. That's what it's like four years on.

At Grantham the sun is shining. Eight minutes until the 11.18 to Wakefield arrives. The lack of sleep is getting to me; I'm yawning. My brain feels like cotton wool. I grab another coffee and take it up the platform as far as the little siding opposite which the Leeds train stops. I start rehearsing the things I've to remember to tell him. Last time they didn't allow me to take in pencil and paper. I'm hearing the train approaching and ticking off points in my head when my eyes stray into the corner of the siding. Just over a year ago, after Siôn lost the first appeal, I saw a discarded newspaper nestling down there, all damp and torn. No print, just a face, Siôn's, looking up at me.

After the appeal I went down to Wales to be with Mum and Dad. One Sunday afternoon, Dad and I drove out to Ystrad Meurig to check on my grandmother's cottage - she was still alive then, staying with family in London. While Dad was in the cottage, I strolled over to Nanna's garage. It's built on the spot where Uncle John the Pipes's *gweithdy* once stood. When he was on bail, Siôn used the garage to revisit his early interest in sculpture. Still there were his chisels, his grinder, his dust-coated radio, and the piece he'd been working on, wrapped in a square of muslin. I lifted the muslin away and looked again at a handsome block of marble, roughly chiselled into a torso. Each tiny hollow in the stone was as individual as a thumbprint. The parings crackled under my feet like frosted leaves. One pictured him here, placing the angle of the blade just so, striking the chisel-butt on this or that side. I picked up one of the parings, and rolled it around my fingers. Siôn was all around me. He had *in extremis* cared for this work.

Outside, with the warmth of the sun on my face, I sat on the grass and looked down towards College Arms, trying to see the village through Siôn's eyes, wondering what he'd felt and thought about over the long hours spent here. And I thought too about Uncle John the Pipes, and his very different kind of life. I tried to imagine what he'd make of it all. It was peaceful, sitting there, and didn't feel in the least bit morbid, but I was glad when Dad locked up the cottage and joined me. I liked hearing his voice calling me 'Llew'. We packed everything in the car and went home.

Outside Wakefield Westgate sits the usual line of bored cab drivers. Breathing short, I head down a herringbone patterned pathway, walking towards a sign for the Unitarian church. At road level I bear right and pass under an iron bridge. Traffic booms along its mixed emptiness of black puddles, dank walls and urine-smell. Another right, opposite the Mercedes showroom, and the prison stretches before me like a great squatting creature: sandy body, grey head.

In the Visitors' Centre I hand over my visitors' slip. The faces of the reception staff are sympathetic, friendly. Good people, I think. Wakefield is a good prison - only a contradiction in terms if you haven't visited Lewes, or Belmarsh, where they sent him after Lewes. Belmarsh was grim. My photograph comes up on a computer screen. I'm given a number. The Visitors' Centre is bright, carpeted and deadly, like a doctor's surgery. Chunky tables and chairs. Lockers. Children's play area. Magazines and a bible. A hatch for coffee and tea. It's 12.30: I can expect to be here for at least an hour. I take five pounds from my wallet, put the wallet back in the coat, and put it and my bag in a locker. The less I take in the better. Most of the people around me I will have seen countless times before. Many expect to be coming here - or somewhere like it - until infirmity strikes, or death releases. Others are waiting for hearings, or appeals, for further appeals, or for miracles. The last thing I want to do is talk to anyone, so I don't sit at a table, but in one of the chairs along the wall. As the time nears, I'm getting jumpy. I take a walk around the room, trying to avoid eyes.

The usual stuff is pinned up on the walls. Same old photo of a sniffer dog - 'I'm good at my job'; Zero Tolerance posters - 'She lives with a successful businessman, loving father... last week he hospitalised her'. All sorts of things on drugs in prison, on bullying and intimidation. And I ask myself, for the thousandth time: What Am I Doing Here?

The answer, as ever, even now, never fails to shock: Siôn is in prison.

My number is called. I'm given an ID badge, with my photo inset, and make my way up along the prison wall to the visitors' entrance. Six or seven of us gather for a few minutes. I start loosening my shoes, like any regular. We're in. I've got the routine by now: shoes off, place in a tray with a belt, watch, ring and jacket. Hand over slip, ID and passport. They've got those things you walk through at airports, that bleep when you leave change in your pocket. I walk through. Raise my arms. I'm frisked, my mouth is checked for drugs, soles of my feet too.

Collect my tray. Put on shoes etc. Door slides open. Door slides shut. Other door slides open.

Clyde the dog - 'I'm good at my job' - stands athwart the route. Walk through, stand on coloured patch of carpet. Door slides shut. Clyde gambols along the line of us, sniffing. His tail's wagging: Clyde gets a real kick out of this. Walk on to the barrier. Hand over slip and ID. They take the slip, hand back the ID. I'm given a table number: 19. I push through a revolving barrier, then through a wooden door into the visiting room.

I'm one of the first. There's no queue at the tea counter, so I buy two coffees and loads of chocolate bars for Siôn. Milky Ways mostly. Room the size of two tennis courts. Lots of square tables, below knee height. Four chairs around each, bolted down. One of them is covered in a red fabric. The prisoner sits there, in sight of the cameras. Primitive mural on the wall. A rostrum for the warders. Prisoners begin to trickle through, their eyes searching for a familiar face. I stare at the mural and wait for Siôn.

We moved around a lot when I was a boy. Dad was doing better and better at work, and every couple of years would be given a promotion. Invariably this meant migrating to a different part of the country. Consequently I attended quite a few schools. One was in Glasgow. I hated every minute of it, but that's besides the point. The point is that on the wall of the

Art Room was a poster of Picasso's *Guernica*. It was the only thing in the whole school I liked. You could have put a bomb under the school, and I'd have lit the fuse, but I loved that picture. I used to stare at it for minutes on end, every art lesson. I'd have been around fourteen, fifteen perhaps.

Once, when I should have been at double maths - I especially hated maths - I went all the way up to the deserted Art Room and spent the best part of two hours smoking cigarettes, chucking pennies against the skirting board and looking up at *Guernica*. But if you'd asked me what it was I liked about the painting, I'd have struggled to give you an answer. I might have mentioned the broken sword, or the horse with the pointy tongue, but the fact is I had absolutely no idea what it all meant. Without understanding the first thing about it, I liked it.

Later, in my early twenties, I read Hugh Thomas's excellent history of the Spanish Civil War. This fomented an interest in all things Spanish, and an early dalliance with Marxism. My new heroes were no longer footballers or writers, but long-dead Spanish republicans of the 1930s, particularly those of a more revolutionary bent, like Delores Ibárruri ['La Pasionaria'] and Andreu Nin. I'd also read about the destruction, in April 1937, of Guernica, the ancient town of the Basques, by Nationalist forces abetted by Nazi Germany. Now, when I looked at *Guernica*, I didn't see a work of art. I saw only an emblem of anti-fascism and democratic freedom, encompassing a collection of ideological rubrics. While belabouring friends with pat explanations of what everything meant ['The horse, you see, represents our shared humanity...'] I'd completely disregard those visceral qualities that had first drawn me to it: its scale, its grotesquerie, its rage and heart-stopping passion. I approached it now as a code breaker, and a rather priggish one at that.

In 1998 I visited Madrid for the first time, and, of course, went to the Reina Sofia to see *Guernica*. Outside, among the bevy of tourists, were stalls selling *Guernica* mugs, *Guernica* pencils, *Guernica* posters and postcards, *Guernica* paperweights. It was hard not to feel dispirited. Inside, I discovered that the museum authorities do not encourage any close, or extended, scrutiny of their golden goose. There's a rail around it, and no seating to be had. I sat on the floor, and was instructed to rise; I pressed as close to the rail as I could, and an alarm went off. The guard looked murderous. I finally claimed a spot centre and front, roughly below the horse with the pointy tongue.

Initially, it's the sheer size of *Guernica* that impresses. You're prepared for it being big, but not that big. On second inspection, however, and beyond that, I felt the painting hadn't really improved much on the posters I'd grown up with. Everything was in place and familiar - far too familiar. There was no sense of the transcendent, no heightened awareness of the power of creation. I felt vaguely aggrieved, as if I'd been brought here under false pretences, and prepared to vacate my spot, to move on to the Mirós and Dalís. And then - then I saw the paint. Specifically, I saw little bobbles of paint around the broken sword, and white paint dripping from the slavering mouth of the horse in agony. I saw brushstrokes. And it seemed to me that I really was seeing the picture complete for the first time, that at last, after twenty-five years, I was sharing fully in its conception, its execution, its emotion: that its essence, its truth as well as its reality, had been revealed to me. And I thought, after all, that you have to get up close to understand. You can't spend your whole life standing back. That day in the Reina Sofia I saw Picasso, a critical eye lifted, white paint dripping from his brush on to his fingers. I saw the paint, and saw the picture, and understood.

The train pulls out of Wakefield two hours late. I don't much care, frankly. The only things that matter on Wakefield days are getting there on time and filling the visit as best you can. As always, I left the prison imagining him by my side, our faces pushed into the wind, headed for a pint at the pub on the corner. Later going for a balti on the pier in Aberystwyth - it's my fantasy, they're my logistics.

Afterwards walking, with waves breaking on the seafront, misting the windscreens of cars; the salt air chill, biting, ocean-fresh.

Lights are flickering in the train carriage. I turn to the window. It offers only darkness and my own reflection. Siôn was fine, more than fine. I've seen all his moods, from black despair to indignation, from abject confusion to phlegmatic fatalism, but today the confidence and swagger were back. That's good. His strength resides in that pocket of his personality. His eyes were bright and clear: good too, means he's sleeping. Grey hair cropped short, skin tight across his cheekbones: a handsome man, smiling and relaxed. I took his lead in conversation. I always do, unless there's something really important to get across. After all, anything we talk about has to go back to the cell with him, while I walk out into the early evening. So we discussed lawyers and appeals, yes, but also books and football and radio programmes. He laughed today. Says he spends most of his time writing letters: to whom he doesn't say. I could worry about that. I probably will, but later. Am I right in thinking his daughters are the only people he's ever really loved? I don't know what made me think of that. No, on second thoughts I'm wrong. A visit lasts two hours, and I'll spend two days going over it in my head.

At Peterborough I give Dad a ring. He picks up straight away: 'Llew? Llew?' Asks how Siôn is, and I say fine, never better. He's pleased, but sounds tired, very tired. This last week he's been as low as I've seen him, barely willing to put one word in front of another, entombed in loss. For him it never stops. What they say about Siôn might not be about him, but it is of him; it speaks directly to his deepest fears, to everything within him that is darkness and confusion. I walk over to the station buffet, thoughts falling like hailstones, hitting hard, all at once resentful of how well Siôn looked. Infidelity hangs in the air like a bad smell. It happens: you're embittered by your constant fears for him, about him, by the sheer amount of time and heartache he absorbs. So - why didn't he ask about Mum and Dad, or me for that matter? I recall how he walked over to the table, glancing at the other prisoners' visitors, gauging the impact of his entrance. Isn't this what he always wanted, everyone's attention? Now it's easy to forget the warmth in his voice, the face resolving itself into courageous lines, the yearning in the eyes that fell on me with an almost bodily impact. Pretty soon I'm blaming him for being Siôn. I want to scream. Quite unexpectedly, but definitely, I hate him.

The bells ring out from St. Michael's and the joint is in the oven! Off to Painswick then, our faces as clear and dauntless as the sun! Pile into the car and collect Mr Pearson from Hucclecote. 'There he is!' - the flat cap, roseate face, corners of his mouth curling under a tooth-brush moustache. He raises a walking stick and Dad makes the ritual show of passing him on the road. Squeals of delight. Have we forgotten to pick him up? - no! It's the same every week and the joke never palls. He climbs into the front seat: 'Pearson here!'

Mr Pearson is retired. Mr Pearson, deliberate charmer and longest serving rep in the history of Michelin Tyres, possibly the world. Good old Bert, tootling round the Cotswolds for over forty years, collecting his orders over long lunches in hand-picked hostelries. Such ropes as he knew he'd shown unendingly to my Dad, his thirty-ish boss. It was a curious alliance: the young-man-in-a-hurry, and the old man with a career of epic mediocrity already behind him, who'd never left home before ten o'clock lest he get caught up in traffic. Perhaps both realised that neither wanted anything from the other besides friendship, or perhaps Dad regarded Mr Pearson as a kind of dodgy inheritance, like a pair of china dogs you never knew what to do with, but, now they're gone, miss seeing around the place.

This morning, as we bowl along towards Painswick, Dad indulges him with a warmed-up slice of office intrigue. Mr Pearson listens, nodding sagely and making his characteristic throat noise, lovingly fashioned in his thorax to indicate anything from deep satisfaction to mild scepticism: 'Hmm *Hmmm*.'

Or, 'Not my favourite person' he might say at the

mention of an old colleague's name. It was the most damning remark I ever heard him utter; no-one ever had such a palpable sense of decorum. This quality comprised much of Mr Pearson's charm, and would only absent itself in his choice of apparel. Today he's wearing a yellow checked waistcoat and a scarlet hat, brought back from his annual trip to a doctor friend in Massachusetts. And, of course, there's his fish tie-clip. It wriggles and swirls, holding Siôn and me in an enveloping spell. Open-mouthed, I flick the tail-fin; the segmented tail wobbles. Mr Pearson chuckles, exposing a section of dazzling false teeth.

The beacon is reached by climbing the flank of a downland hill on the edge of a golf course. A wagtail is dusting its feathers in a bunker. Mr Pearson and Dad swish their sticks: *thwack* goes one thistle, *thwack* goes another, sailing away over a ditch brimming with red campion and nestling in the light rough. Startled, the wagtail banks and veers across the soft turf - *chizzick chizzick* - and a purple-faced golfer halts at the top of his swing. But now the beacon is in sight and Dad and Siôn make a race of it. At last, Mr Pearson brings out the Thornton's, humbugs or mintoes, and the grown-ups sigh at a vista of summery fairways, upland and valley. Cloud shadows march towards us, gathering speed as sunlight glows cowslip yellow on our skin.

Then home to the residential slopes of our little suburbia, with its car washing and aroma of charcoal, testing the roast as the Yorkshires rise to *Two-Way Family Favourites*. Mr Pearson peers into the bubbling froth for the cauli he brought, while we study a bottle of wine, sickly sweet white, giggling at our worldliness. Dad opens it like an unexploded bomb. Mum calls: 'It's ready!' and we switch off the radiogram, and Mr Pearson, for whom the growing of cauliflowers is art, yes, and science too, is soon spearing the first creamy floret:

'Hmm *Hmmmm*. From the garden, *of course*.'

Late afternoon on the front lawn and I'm feeling the drag of the day. I've sorted through my Monkees cards. Peter Tork is missing. Now it's time for *Champion the Wonder Horse*, absolutely my favourite television programme, but Dad and Siôn are still in the sitting room. I glower across the indolent buzzing of the garden, through the spindly branches of a sapling Mum planted in our first Gloucestershire spring. It's the same every Sunday: my brother confounded by fractions, baffled by long division, taking up the whole afternoon. Today he's learning to tie a tie.

Going in, I glimpse Mum's tightening face and know something's up. Siôn sits in a corner of the settee. We exchange quick trapped looks, but lowering my lids like a criminal I tie the tie as requested. He looks at me as if I alone had found the secret of being loved; then, thick-fingered, tries it himself, a torrent of blood swarming to his cheeks.

He never gave in, and hardly cried at all, and with a weight of guilt banging in my stomach I wandered along the lane to the waterfall, where I sat in the grass and stared down at a dead cat, lying on the rocks like a sodden jumper.

There was a family wedding in Gloucestershire a while back. Mum, Dad and I went down. That morning we took a couple of hours and went to visit Mr Pearson's grave, in a little churchyard a stone's throw from his vegetable patch. We saw too our old house, looking so small now. The sapling I peered through that afternoon had grown into a huge tree, towering above the surrounding roofs, throwing its shadow over the little semi and the lives that had once existed there. As we got back to the car, it started to rain. We drove off with the windscreen wipers slapping back and forth, wiping it all away. When I got home, I wrote to Siôn about what I had seen and felt and remembered. I kept the letter a week or so, changing bits here and there. Then I tore it up. Maybe that was for the best, but it didn't feel like anything to be proud of.

On the Norwich train I sit across and back along the aisle from a plain girl with bad spots. She's about seventeen. A guy of forty-ish comes on at Thetford. Starts talking to her. Cheerful, plausible tones. She's shy; her face burns. He's awkward to begin with, but seeing how shy she is gives him confidence. He starts telling jokes, making tiny supplementary gestures with his hands. When he laughs, his laughter sounds strained, with a slightly unnerving edge to it. She begins to laugh with him, seeing as there's no-one in the carriage to see her laughing - you know how shy people are. Then, just out of Attleborough, he asks her where she lives. She says Norwich. I do too, he says, whereabouts in Norwich? She tells him. I know what's coming, and I think maybe she does too. He offers her a lift home from the station. He's smiling still, teeth like piano keys, but you can see the wanting, the desperation in his eyes. She says yes, but only because she's a shy girl. Everything changes. Her smile disappears. You can sense her resentment. They've only been talking ten minutes. And you can see she's thinking that if she hadn't been a plain girl with bad spots, but a beautiful girl with clear skin, he'd have never dared to ask her such a thing after ten minutes: him being old enough to be her father, and with that horrible pleading look in his eyes. He tries to start up his routine again, but it's too late. All that's left is her fear and his desperation.

At Norwich I hang back as everyone else collects their things. I'm still in Wakefield, among the iron rooms, sliding doors and blocked imperatives. I get off when the engines die. Halfway down the platform, behind a bunch of football supporters, I see the shy girl stop, say something to the man and disappear by herself into the station buffet. He wavers for a second or two, shoulders racked, then moves off slowly. As I pass the buffet, I look in. She's in there all right, standing back from the big window, watching her erstwhile suitor recede into the night. I'm glad. I'm glad she's been careful. She looks a good person, and good people have to go carefully in a world like this. Outside the station it's drizzling again.

I reach the car cold and damp, and with a headful of bad conscience. Outside Norwich, near Hedenham, I take a short cut down one of the little back lanes. My car hits a muddy bank and goes into a long skid. The engine cuts out. I'm slewing from one side to the other, then I'm spun across the lane and end up at right angles to the opposite bank, my rear wheels pressed into the hedgerow. I sit there for maybe five minutes, enervated and hyper all at once.

It's a tiny lane; there's no-one else around, no houses. No sound. Siôn's with me, floating in and out of my mind, keeping me company. I get out of the car and walk down the road a spell, my legs still a little rocky. I'm saying sorry. Walking into the darkness and saying sorry, calling it out, right out loud. Sorry for not loving him as generously or fluently as I ought to have done, over all the years he might have needed me. Sorry for standing back. I must only have walked about a hundred yards, but when I turn around I can't see my car anymore. No lights on these roads. I follow the line of the bank back to the car. I try the ignition. No good. Strange thing, I'm not at all bothered. Then, after ten minutes or so, I remember to press the button in the boot, the one that does something to the fuel pump. I finally get home around midnight. Once there, I sit in the dark and drink tea and listen to the shipping forecast, thinking of little boats, miles and miles apart, tossed around on black and stormy seas.

Part Five

PELICAN, SHADOW AND PINCHED STONE

This wasn't normal. I knew it as soon as my eyes opened. Before, probably. I sat bolt upright, breathing fast, much too fast. I felt dizzy. I was covered in sweat. I jumped out of bed and started walking, out of the bedroom, into the hallway, into the kitchen: walking quickly, trying to keep pace with my crazily pounding heart. It was October 2001, seven o'clock in the morning, and I thought I was going to die. I thought I was going to die alone. I called an ambulance. That thought, the thought that I was going to die, lasted a few seconds, maybe a minute. It lasted until I realised that people having heart attacks don't run around, don't call ambulances, didn't, I supposed, think of very much at all. But my heart was still banging away, and there was still an awful lot to figure out, so I sat on the sofa and made a start.

I hadn't been sleeping well. I'd been working late. I hadn't eaten till gone nine. I'd drunk the best part of a bottle of red wine. Well, there you are then, hardly the great mystery illness. As the ambulance men approached the front door, my face was already prickling with embarrassment. But they were fine about it, these two good men doing a job they cared about. They gave me a

133

cardiograph test, took my blood pressure, and insisted I'd done the right thing in calling for them: 'You can't be too careful', stuff like that. I chipped in with the odd self-deprecating comment, looked sheepish and laced the comments and the looks with boneheaded cheerfulness. The tests told me I was fine. I'd had a panic attack, that's all, except the ambulance men didn't say that's all. They sympathised. The younger one told me he'd had one when he was younger. I made them a cup of tea. I asked them about their job. I listened attentively to their replies. I'm a good listener, and the younger one in particular was more than happy to talk.

I waved goodbye to them from my front lawn, feeling idiotic and at the same time mightily relieved. Ahead of me lay nine months of breakdown and recovery from breakdown.

Fear creeps in as the evening shadows deepen. A twinge of anxiety becomes an ache. My demons, having struck first in bed, seem content - for now at least - to stay put, like an occupying force establishing a bridgehead. Only at bedtime do the familiar symptoms start to reappear: the parched mouth, the churning stomach, the racing heart, cold sweats, heart shakes, and something like a hot ball of wax lodging itself behind my breast bone. Battle has been joined. I'm at war with my own body, trying to outflank one attack, double-bluffing another, all the

134

time constructing strange formulas and rituals to repel pike-runs into my fevered brain.

I settle into a foetal position, my cardigan pulled around me, my knees pushing a hot water bottle into my midriff. Alongside my bed is a bowlful of cold water, with a flannel ready to be dragged across my face. On the wardrobe opposite the bed I've blu-tacked bits of paper carrying messages copied from self-help books. These I gaze at between sips of water and almost as many visits to the toilet. My pillows are arranged to block out the sound of my heart. I worry about it running too slow; I worry about it running too fast; I worry about it stopping altogether. Then I start breathing too deeply, too quickly, and start hyperventilating again. Last night I ran out into the back garden and threw myself onto the grass. It was three o'clock in the morning. There I knelt, freezing cold, my knees sinking into the mud, gulping for air. I rubbed dew over my face. I looked up at the stars. I said 'Help'. Not shouted, that word, but whispered. When I'd calmed down, I crawled back inside and ran a hot bath. Sitting in the muddy bathwater, I glimpsed my reflection in the bathroom mirror. My throat seemed to shut and I began to sob. It was like unblocking a secret drain inside my chest. And I thought: this feels better. Here at last is something I can do to make myself feel better.

At what point I had begun to disintegrate I can't say

for sure. I'd always understood, and this with absolute certainty, that no matter how tough things got in the general run, I could always find something new, something special, to feel good about. But I hadn't known that kind of certainty in a long time. Days melting into weeks, weeks into months - a swamp of years into which I sank like a car wreck, disappearing slowly. I distilled my activities down to the things I had to do, or did instinctively, without thought and without meaning attached. I saw the people closest to me less and less, and others not at all. Hairline cracks, now a canyon, separating my mind from my body.

Since my brother's arrest, I'd been keeping a journal, recording and reflecting on events as a defence against being overwhelmed by them. About ten days before the onset of my breakdown, I read everything I'd written over the last four years. I concluded that despite its many weaknesses and omissions, the account as it stood had a natural shape and unity to it, and that I should stop writing. Besides - this is the way I was thinking - perhaps churning out this stuff was perpetuating a sense of being hard-done-by. It was time to move on. What to move on to, though? I couldn't find my way back to my old life, that's for sure. I was a different man now. And without the daily discipline of going to my writing desk, I had no mechanism through which to express my thoughts, my fears, my sometimes crippling sadness. I felt its lack profoundly, without at first recognising the fact.

Furthermore, on re-reading my journal, what struck me most forcibly was my own invisibility from the events that had so disfigured my life. I sensed that here, behind the writing, was a personality wholly at odds with itself. My behaviour since Siôn's arrest simply reflected my role within the family: the peace maker, the unifying element, the good listener, never judging, always willing to compromise, an open space into which others could vent their sorrows and frustrations. Which is okay up to a point, but you can lose yourself in there. At this remove I had no confidence in my ability to express anything that was true to myself. Sure, I could graft on a few opinions, and they'd sound right enough, but I had no bedrock of personal conviction on which to plant my feet, lift my chin and say: 'This is me, this is where I stand.' I'd played my role for too long. I was gone. Lost to evasion and to shame.

I'm barefoot, padding at half-trot around the silent, moonlit garden. I'm thinking about my brother. My glands pump adrenalin like bad alcohol, befuddling my senses and rotting my faith in myself. I'm afraid of my own body, of my inability to control its responses. I fear a door has been opened in my brain that I'll never be able to close, completely, again. Across the threshold lies the pit of mental illness.

My home that I have loved is now my prison, a place of bleakness and confusion, and no rest. I'm snapped out of sleep by grotesque terrors, formless creatures. Halfway up a rise, crawling through heavy sweating grass, I see yellow eyes, malignant in their impassivity, staring out at me through parted bracken. I'm ambushed by distressing memories. I try desperately to create nothing in my brain, to expel all thought, lest the shards of breakdown slip back in. But it's no use. Yesterday, driving out to meet a client, I took a wrong turn near Bury St. Edmunds; I did a U-turn across the dual carriageway, screaming silently, braced for the impact of metal against metal. I'm not safe. Friends say it's all in my head; but I am my head; what's in my head is who I am; if it's in my head it's me.

Now it's no longer just the nights. Pulses beat in my throat, choking me. I'm about to jump out of an aircraft: every minute's that way; the fear is pressing in on me; I want to jump, but can't. I never jump. Never land. It's just the fear for me. The lump in my throat - is it cancer? Headaches at night - a tumour? My eyelids won't shut. See, I'm trying to shut them, but I can't. I'll never be able to close my eyelids again. Why can't I stop myself hiccupping? I can't stop going to the toilet; I'm incontinent. I'll soil myself soon, I know I will. Are my kidneys packing up, my lungs?

How do you breathe? I've forgotten how to breathe. I behold a flash of myself in the grave.

The house is very cold. It is 3.00am and I'm sitting on the floor, waiting for the doctor to ring me back. I'm getting to be one of their regulars. I used to be a Samaritan. I too had my regulars and my bunch of files. I wonder if I was any good. Was I calm and responsive? - vague on occasions, a little complacent? - or was I clipped and judgemental, a bit of a smart-arse? I can't recall. I'm broken now. I want to be taken into hospital, to be sectioned. I want clean linen sheets; I want a calm and responsive doctor, examining a clipboard at the bottom of my bed. Like Ronald Colman had in *Random Harvest*. I remember watching that movie on television. I was fine then.

Running through the night, but I can't run any more. The beta-blockers have kicked in. I'm shaking with cold and exacerbated nerves. I turn homeward, but there's a headwind now. It cuts into my face. I'm trying to keep my mouth shut, but I'm panting, because of the beta-blockers, and the wind is stealing all my breath, freezing my toiling lungs. I'll never make it. My home is only two hundred yards away; I can see its lights, but I can't move. I want to lie down, here by the roadside, and be frozen. Freeze the fear and let it fall away. A buffet of wind almost blows me off my feet. I go on; I get there; I ring for the doctor. He comes out to me, says he'll give me a shot that will knock me out for six to eight hours. I take a pill first, then he gives me the shot. Blessed sleep envelopes me.

Why am I awake? Why isn't it morning? I can feel my mouth trembling. I reach for my watch and snap on the bedside light. I've slept for less than an hour. Blood is coursing in my head. My limbs are damp with sweat. I want to weep, but can't. A pity, because weeping has become one of my things.

A beta-blocker in the morning, followed by an anti-depressant. Two Librium twice a day and four at night, plus two sedative pills. I was on Prozac, but it left me chewing the wallpaper. The wall of my chest is still aching, like it's been scrubbed raw. I'm at Celia's. Celia is my best friend. She gives me hot milk before bed. When I'm awake in the early hours she talks to me, holding my hand: I'm propped up in a reclining chair. Right now there aren't too many things in life worth a damn, but her friendship is one of them. I'm staying here a week, then going to my parents' in Wales. I can't be alone anymore. My doctor has put me on Norfolk Mental Health's care register. A psychiatric nurse is coming to see me tomorrow. She sounded nice on the 'phone, but I used to work in mental health care. Mental health meant other people.

PELICAN, SHADOW AND PINCHED STONE

Yesterday we went for a walk: Celia, her husband Gerry and me. Down a country lane we came across a group of twitchers, all tooled up with binoculars, telescopes and notebooks. In hushed tones they explained that a badly off-course pelican had landed on the marshes - from Serbia, apparently. I caught a glimpse of its flapping wings in the tall grasses. Then I asked Celia if we could turn back. Amongst that throng of people, all happy, smiling, engaged with their hobby, I felt more incongruous than a Serbian pelican on the Norfolk marshes.

I can't stand the noise - all noise, any noise. Last night the distant bark of a dog kept me awake and jittery long after it had ceased to bark, the bark continuing to exist as a reverberation. A toot of a car horn, a crash of gears, even the scrape of a knife on a plate: all of these can invoke near panic. Walking through the park, a splutter of fireworks had me diving into a hedge like some shell-shocked infantryman. My brain burned for hours afterwards.

I'm in Aberystwyth. At night I wander my parents' house, a Bedouin with a duvet. I take any sleep the pills give me upstairs; then I rest on the sofa downstairs until dawn, or pace the corridors and kitchen. I'm taking my pulse constantly. It isn't the sound of life, but of inescapable death.

I'm walking along Great Darkgate Street in

Aberystwyth, blinking rain out my eyes. I can hardly comprehend my surroundings or the direction I'm taking. My hand is over my heart; I feel its beat with my fingers. I can't go home. I can't let my parents see me like this. And still the drenching rain drifts in from the sea, winking in the streetlights, disappearing into lighted shop windows. Outside Lunn Poly a spasm shoots across my chest. I wince and tears well up. I don't want to exist anymore, not in this quaking, pathetic version of myself. I can't lift the umbrella anymore, but I walk on anyway, away from the shops and towards the sea. The night is coating my brain, my soul; it's filling me up, squeezing me out, taking me away into the blackness of the sea. I can't hold on anymore. I'm alone, cast out and apart.

Emerging out of the sea mist is the north tower of the castle ruins, and beyond that the tawny stonework of the Anglican church. Further along I can see stone steps leading up to the church, but ignore these and try clambering up a shallow bank. My foot slips. I just fail to keep my balance and fall back into the road. A car horn blares behind me. Someone shouts. I pick myself up and look out to sea. Everything is intensely quiet. I register not being able to hear the hush of the waves breaking on the shore. Something's out there, something vaguely remembered: it's in me too, trembling on the edge of exultation, too vast to contain or to understand.

Ancient images sink into my mind and into my body, and I know, in these moments, that I'm going to let go of fear: this tumorous fear which invades me at night; that grows again upon waking; that starts in my stomach and bleeds into the confluence between mind and feeling; that makes it impossible for me to cross any line of judgement; that erodes my sense of wonder and purpose, and makes me doubt the things in myself I'd always thought of as the best of myself...

Only by releasing this fear can I start to confront the greater fear: the fear of obscurity, cold and dreadful, that goes with long-term spiritual defeat. Only then will the gentle ordinariness of life be vouchsafed me once again. I see all this with utter clarity, and am unafraid. My past, present and future seem to coalesce in the air around me, and the discord between my mind and body falls away like spent time. I'm not sure if I stood there for seconds or minutes, but that night, when I went to bed, I decided not to fight the symptoms of my illness, but instead to accept them, and let them flow over me. And slowly I began to see the possibility of another kind of life. Not my old life back again, but something new, devoid of confusion and despair, attached to a perennial certitude. It was the beginning of getting well. I knew things that night. I felt invulnerable. And although the night went, and this knowledge with it, my daily terrors, though present for a deal longer, would never seem quite so terrifying again. The road before me was open, and, if the road kept on running, time couldn't run out.

Tensed muscles. The side of my head throbbing. My will to act paralysed. Hang on to an image. The petals of the flower on the mantelpiece. Trace the shapes in my mind. My eyelids are springing open. I'm blinking maniacally. Petals on the mantelpiece. Concentrate. Take everything else away. I'll never be able to shut my eyes again. I'll stick them down with masking tape. Petals, think, think. Garlands of mulberries around a pale blue door. White camellias. Calico. What's that? - an iron bridge, over water, with meadow land beyond the bank. A boy is standing in the shadow of a two-trunked birch, gazing into the fast-running brook. I can't see his features, only his waxen complexion. Bright, metallic colours, everywhere, like Kodachrome. I expect to hear birdsong, but there's silence, utter silence, apart from the boy's breathing, which is my breathing too. A lovely carillon chimes music I cannot hear, but feel. Throw something back; throw your heart and pierce the echoes. The Lady Chapel at Ely, ethereally-lit. Sun-bars across crumbling stonework, leading to the misty edge of sleep. Blue dress. Stay there, stay. Elaine Duncan, sitting next to me at Kilbarchan Primary. Church-pale face. Soap and toothpaste. She smiles, glances sideways and away, then with a gesture of caution leans forward. Sunlight, falling from the big window, touches her pale gold hair. Slipping away now. Going on despite defeat, that's the thing. I slept for three hours last night. I'll do better tonight.

I disinter another memory, a familiar one, only this time it's different, beyond simple remembrance. Beyond, it seems to me, even my perception of the event as I lived it. Certainly beyond any effort of imagination. The scene as reconstructed now seems imbued with a kind of hyper-reality: it's like putting one of those grids over a painting in order to study its detail. When you take the grid away, you see new depths to the painting; you discover new meanings, new explanations. Perhaps the medication I'm taking plays a part in this percipience of senses and instinct, but not, I think, too much of one. I revisit this Segovian episode, or parts of it, most nights, and sometimes during the day, when I'm walking along the seashore. Its qualities are intensely personal, somewhat arcane in one or two of its minor details, but with the force of good scripture running through it like a heartbeat...

It was late in the evening. I'd had a couple of hours in the bars, and I wanted to clear my head, so I went to sit on the steps at the high end of the Roman aqueduct, overlooking the Plaza del Azoguejo. A hazy weft of violet shadows was falling away from the aqueduct towards the Plaza de la Artilleria. They've been falling that way for more than two thousand years. My own shadow was rising up two granite blocks at the base of one of the lower arches. The Romans hoisted each block into place with hooks: no mortar was used. The whole thing stays up by the weight of one stone pushing against another. The grip-holes for the hooks are still there. You can see them clearly, like pinches in dough.

There was a flash of white as a stork banked over the upper tier of arches; I shielded my eyes against the sun and lost it, then saw it again, folding its wings on a chimneypot near the Mesón de Cándido. It stayed there a long time, watching me as I watched the sun settle into the valley. I saw the last tourist take his last photograph. I saw the woman from the Bureau de Change lock up, saw the lights go on in the Mesón de Cándido, and heard Cathedral bells summoning the faithful to mass. I saw the *mudéjar* tower of San Martin turning to gold. Below me, on the bottom step, two boys taunted a rib-thin dog by lobbing pebbles on to its back. When one hit its nose, the boys laughed and the dog skulked away, watching them from a safe distance, confused by their cruelty but needing someone to belong to.

I saw some workmen who had been working on the aqueduct gather beneath one of its central arches to roll cigarettes and talk about the day's work. They talked most seriously, not bantering at all, giving the work its proper respect. As the sky melted into twilight, they made their last points with little jabs of fingers and cigarettes before heading homeward, each taking a separate path, leaving their threads of smoke licking the underside of the arch.

By the time I saw Meadow circling the middle of the plaza, her eyes searching for me in the heavy shadows, every arch on the aqueduct seemed to offer a window on all time. As the air rose around me in a flowering breeze, I fancied it carried echoes of other lives, lives as fleeting as mine, and Meadow's, and the workmen's. Only the aqueduct would remain after all, standing sharp at dawn or cloaked in the dead blue dusk. Vehement with aspiration, lifted by endurance, and scarce breathing, I had an incredible sense of connectedness. I was part of everything I saw around me. I was in the curve of the arch, in the weft of shadows, in the flash of the stork's wing, in everything that existed and would ever exist. The tumult in my head ceased. My heart, pallid for so long, stirred again with vivid colours. And I knew, as I descended the steps and Meadow took my hand - this is by no means easy to express - that nothing that moves us is ever lost, or is rendered valueless by time; that love withstands all that is done against it; and that all our roads are the same road, under the same sky.

It was getting late, but Meadow wasn't hungry and I was still drowsy with wine, so we walked the length of the aqueduct, weaving between the arches and pressing our palms and foreheads to the cool stone. When we arrived at a sloping square near the Calle de Almira, Meadow decided to teach me to sing. We lay on our backs in the fitful glare of a streetlight and cast mangled scales into the depths of the Castilian night. A few yards away, a cat - female, old, slack-bellied - glanced at us with austere politeness, then went back to inspecting scraps outside a small red-tiled house, dividing strips of fat from rotting cabbage with a fastidiously raised paw.

As we headed back into town, I heard the squeal of a window followed by a high-pitched curse. I looked back to see the cat caught in a dull patch of light from an upstairs room. With tired interest she gazed up at her accuser before selecting a morsel of food and moving stiffly away. She settled against the foot of a shallow arch: unable to be humiliated, completely unconquerable.

In attempting to draw a bead on the contradictions and longings of the last few years, I have read much, observed much in others, thought about it all until my brain ached, and been wide of the mark in nearly all of my conclusions. This book is a record, mostly, of confusion. I can't say what readers, if such there be, might gain from it. I hope it might encourage some to try and embody their own best instincts. I hope that others, those who have been brought to the edge themselves, might avoid - as I so singularly failed to do - the constant observation of their own suffering. If one can tear oneself away from oneself, and concentrate instead on the exterior world, with all its life and beauty, and in all its diversity, then truth and resolution will surely follow.

All I can really say, however, is that this experience is my own.

Epilogue

Last summer, Mum, Dad and I went out for a meal. It was a mild Aberystwyth evening, so we walked home through the park, under a soft light of stars. I thought how good the National Library looked, a neoclassical pile, lit up on its hill. Then straight away I felt heavy-hearted, thinking about the times Siôn and I had climbed up there while he was on bail; thinking of his different time now, stuck in prison, time just reference points on a damned clock. But as I walked on, my mind began to weave among other kinds of thoughts: sad, yes, of course, but happy too, and bittersweet. After all, that time wasn't lost, we'd had it, lived it, enjoyed each other's company in a way we hadn't for years. This mood of pleasurable sorrow deepened. I looked over at my parents: the white of their hair, my Dad's limp, my Mum's dipping strides, arms folded. And suddenly the whole weight of the firmament was barely equal to the love I felt for them. Since my brother's imprisonment I'd become more conscious than ever of the passage of time. I knew that part of this consciousness was a growing realisation that my parents might never again see Siôn outside a prison. But there was another part: a fear that one day my memory of them would fade to the point I couldn't see them anymore. And I was aware for the first time of taking mental pictures of them, preserving the

151

moment, so to speak, storing it away, as insurance against a time when they wouldn't be here, knowing that however lonely, or cold, or strained within I felt, I could always come back to this moment. It would be my way of keeping faith with them. My way of keeping us all together.

They started talking about the garden. Mum wanted to start a spice bed, and to clip back the wisteria. Dad wanted to paint the ironwork. I walked behind them, tasting my gladness, feeling the texture of the material inside my pocket, and smelling the air, redolent of the sweetness of honeysuckle.

Ceredigion, 2002